Meteorological Satellites

William K. Widger, Jr.

Coordinating Editor:
James V. Bernardo, Director
Educational Programs and Services
National Aeronautics and Space Administration

 Holt, Rinehart and Winston, Inc., New York

William K. Widger, Jr. is Director of Satellite Meteorology Research, ARACON Geophysics Company, Concord, Mass.

He was born in Lynn, Mass., graduated from the University of New Hampshire, and was granted a ScD in Meteorology at MIT. After teaching at Cornell University and a tour of active duty with the USAF, he held several responsible positions resulting in his appointment as Chief, Operational Meteorological Programs, in Headquarters of the National Aeronautics and Space Administration.

Dr. Widger is a Fellow of the American Association for the Advancement of Science and holds membership in the American Meteorological Society, American Geophysical Union, Sigma Xi, and the Scientific Research Society of America. He is the author of many scientific reports and articles in a dozen different scientific journals, and has chaired or served on numerous governmental and scientific society committees.

Original drawings: Versatron Corporation

Preface

In the early hours of April 1, 1960, engineers, technicians, and scientists were working diligently at widely scattered locations.

At Cape Canaveral, the countdown of a Thor-Able launch vehicle was nearing its end; under the protective shroud was a 270-pound spacecraft which would make history and start a new era in perhaps the oldest of the natural sciences—meteorology.

A second location was a space data acquisition facility at Kaena Point, Oahu, Hawaii—a mountain top overlooking the central Pacific. History had been made here before when an American radar had picked up the Japanese aircraft approaching Pearl Harbor. The primitive radar that had stood there in 1941 had long since been replaced, and a huge 60-foot antenna now dominated the area. But not everything was modern; the scientists who would work on the data found their task made more difficult by the drafts inherent in a canvas-covered Jamesway hut of World War II vintage exposed to the steady trade winds.

A third group manned a station at a modern industrial plant at Hightstown, New Jersey. A fourth monitored the status of events in an office building a few blocks from the White House. Others were making final adjustments to equipment at the several NASA Minitrack Stations in Florida, California, South America, and Australia.

For many of these people, today would culminate years of intense effort. But that day would mark not only success beyond all expectation, but the beginning of even more intensive activities. As they worked, several wondered if there was any significance to the fact that it was April Fool's Day. Others suggested that Ground Hog's Day would have been appropriate.

Still another group manned a third data acquisition station at Belmar, New Jersey. Some occupied a historic site—the building from which some of the first trans-Atlantic wireless messages were transmitted in the early 1900's. Within hours, these people would

3

be the first ever to see clear pictures of the earth and its clouds televised from over 400 miles in space. Later, the best of these pictures would be shown to the President of the United States. The satellite launched that day was TIROS I, and from then on meteorology would never be quite the same.

It was my privilege to be at Belmar on that historic day and to have seen those first television cloud pictures while the film was still damp. Among them were photographs of cloud cover associated with storms off the New England coast and over the Mississippi Valley. Before the next day was done, I would be seeing pictures of the Red Sea, the Dead Sea, Cyprus, Italy, and a great storm in the Atlantic. Since then, hundreds of thousands of pictures of the earth's weather have been taken over all areas from Greenland to Antarctica. Additional photographs are constantly providing us with new information on the weather. They are also presenting us with new questions we must answer to understand the ever-changing atmosphere and to better our ability to forecast the weather. TIROS has now moved from a novelty to a routine operation, and has been joined in its tasks by Nimbus; nevertheless, the fascination of its data, and of the complexity of its equipment, is hardly dimmed.

April 1, 1960, marked a milestone toward which I, along with thousands of others, had worked for five years. But, looking both backward and forward, it was only a milestone. In the years since, TIROS and the programs that have developed from it have continued as my vocation with no decrease in challenge or interest. Nor does the road ahead appear less promising.

In this volume, I have the privilege to lead you again over the trail that lies behind and to point out the highway that remains to be built ahead. I will attempt to illustrate what we can see in the pictures TIROS provides, what it takes to get them, and how they are used. But TIROS is not the end; it has its inherent deficiencies which it is expected that Nimbus and other future meteorological satellites will overcome. These future satellites lie somewhere ahead of us on a highway whose direction can only be indicated. But I hope some of you may be inspired to join in the task of building one of the many roads to a better future.

Contents

To my wife, Connie, and my daughters, Dorothy and Barbara Louise. In common with the families of so many of the scientists and engineers concerned with the meteorological satellite program, they have too often suffered as my full attention was distracted from family matters by the demands and fascinations of the weather satellite systems and their data.

1

What Meteorological Satellites See

Somewhere in the distant past—presumably more than 100,000 years ago but probably later than 1,000,000 B.C.—a man, for the first time, climbed high enough on a mountain to see the landscape spread out before him. Man is inherently curious about natural conditions, and it is reasonable to assume that this first mountaineer looked at a hawk soaring above him and wondered how the earth would look if he had the power to reach still greater altitudes. Perhaps it was that day when a man climbed high enough on a day when low-level clouds hid some of the landscape below. Again, natural curiosity may have led him to wonder what forms the clouds would take if viewed from far above.

But many ages were to pass before these questions could be answered. First, curiosity on these matters would be intensified when Galileo invented the telescope and discovered that the moon also had mountains, plains which he mistook for seas, and numerous large and small craters whose origin is not fully resolved, even by the excellent pictures taken by Ranger. A step in the right direction came in the late eighteenth century with the invention of the balloon, but for decades balloon altitudes would not significantly exceed the heights of the higher mountains. Only with the twentieth century and the invention of aircraft would the first spectacular views of the earth and its cloud cover be possible.

But technology progresses at an ever-accelerating rate. It took man hundreds of thousands of years to reach altitudes of tens of thousands of feet. Yet only a few decades more were needed to extend attainable altitudes to hundreds of miles. In the late 1940's, the first photographs of our planet and its cloud patterns from outer space were taken from research rockets

Fig. 1-1. A TIROS IV view of the Great Lakes taken during April 1962. (TIROS photograph)

fired at White Sands, New Mexico. Areas with a radius of over 500 miles were seen, but only in the vicinity of a very few rocket ranges and only infrequently.

It was not until the launch of TIROS I (Television and InfraRed Observation Satellite), in April 1960, that it became possible to monitor weather conditions from outer space on a regular basis and over most of the world.

In a subsequent chapter, we will review more fully parts of the history of these tremendous improvements in our capability to observe the weather. Interesting as that story is, of far greater fascination are the pictures provided by TIROS and NIMBUS (Chapter 10).

TIROS was designed to obtain cloud pictures, but on the average only about one-half of the earth is cloud covered. Accordingly, TIROS frequently photographs geographic features of our planet. Let us start with a few of these pictures, the familiar areas which will help in acquiring a feel for the scale and size of features in the pictures against later discussions of cloud patterns where landmarks are often hidden by the clouds. As we study these pictures, it will be helpful to have a good world altas or globe handy for comparison purposes.

Some TIROS Photographs

Starting first in the United States, Figure 1-1 is a vivid view of the Great Lakes as seen by TIROS IV in April 1962. Lake Michigan is to the left of the picture center, with Lake Superior to its upper left, and Lakes Huron, Erie, and part of Lake Ontario to the right. Southeastern Lake Huron and northern Lake Erie are hidden by clouds. Other clouds can be seen west of Lake Michigan, northeast of Lake Huron, and south of Lakes Erie and Ontario. Northwest of Lake Superior is the white, ice-covered Lake Nipigon.

Moving southeast, Figure 1-2 shows Florida as it appeared

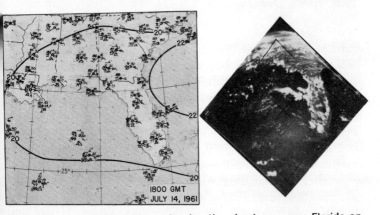

Fig. 1-2. A TIROS III picture showing thunderstorms over Florida on July 14, 1961. (USWB)

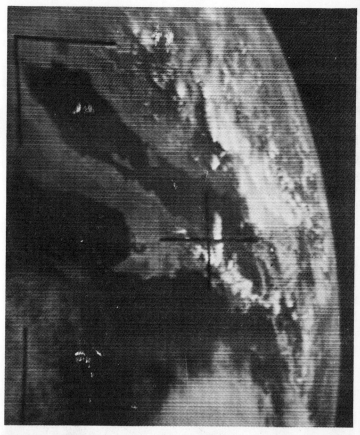

Fig. 1-3. A TIROS V picture of Baja California and the Gulf of California. Clouds can be seen over Mexico and the Pacific Ocean. (TIROS photograph)

to TIROS III on July 14, 1961. At this time, the peninsula was covered by a number of major thunderstorms, as shown by the bright white patches which indicate the towering cumulonimbus clouds. A continuous line of these clouds forms a squall line extending west of Tampa, into the Gulf of Mexico. However, most of the shoreline is clearly visible, as is Lake Okeechobee.

On the west coast of North America, Baja California is

frequently seen by TIROS, as in Figure 1-3, which shows this long peninsula and the Gulf of California to its east.

Farther north along the Pacific coast, Figure 1-4 shows northern California. Near the center of the picture is San Francisco Bay; the brightness of the water of the bay and of the ocean just off the Golden Gate is a sun glint. These occur when the direction of the camera view and the position of the sun are such that the picture includes the reflection of the sun from a comparatively calm body of water. East of San Francisco Bay, the gray area is the lighter earth of the cultivated areas in the San Joaquin Valley. Still farther east, the bright white areas are snows on the Sierra Nevadas. Careful examination of the outline of the snow areas suggest the snow cover at this time was confined to altitudes of about 10,000 feet and

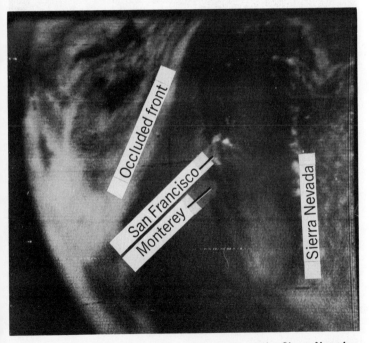

Fig. 1-4. California, San Francisco Bay, snow on the Sierra Nevadas, and clouds over the Pacific. (TIROS photograph)

higher. Far out to sea are the clouds of a major storm system.

Moving to more distant lands, the highly reflective sands of the desert areas of North Africa and the Near East have provided striking satellite pictures. Typical are those of the northern portions of the Nile River and the Red Sea, as illustrated in Figure 1-5, where the Nile (accentuated by the vegetation along it) and its delta, the Red Sea, the Gulf of Aqaba, and the Dead Sea are obvious.

Figure 1-5a is an even more detailed Nimbus picture of the same area, taken when the Nile was flooding its valley.

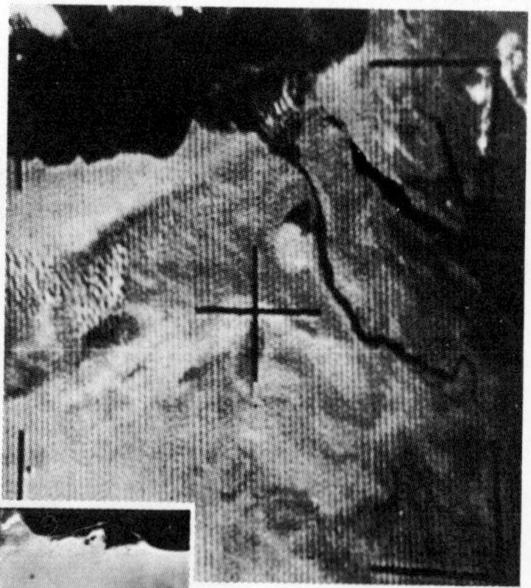

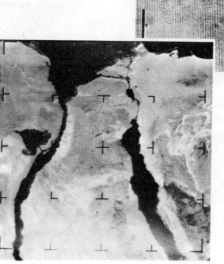

Fig. 1-5. Egypt, the Nile and its delta, the Red Sea, the Gulf of Aqaba, and the Dead Sea. (TIROS photograph)

Fig. 1-5a. A Nimbus picture of the Nile at flood stage, September 1964. (NASA)

Fig. 1-6. A mosaic of TIROS pictures showing the entire Red Sea, and portions of the Mediterranean and the Gulf of Aden. (USWB)

Fig. 1-7. Great Britain (partially cloud covered), Ireland, the English Channel, and France. (TIROS photograph)

Figure 1-6 is a mosaic (a matching together) of several TIROS pictures starting with approximately this same area of Egypt and running down the entire Red Sea to the Gulf of Aden. Various degrees of cloudiness can be seen over the land areas.

Figure 1-7 takes us to northwest Europe. Great Britain is covered with broken clouds, but its coast lines, Ireland, the English Channel, and northwestern France can be identified. Widespread cloudiness exists southwest and west of the British Isles.

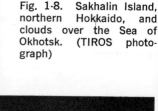

Fig. 1-8. Sakhalin Island, northern Hokkaido, and clouds over the Sea of Okhotsk. (TIROS photograph)

Fig. 1-9. Shark Bay and North West Cape, Australia. (TIROS photograph)

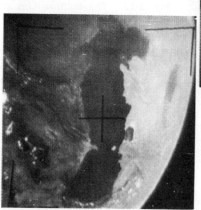

Fig. 1-10. The Caspian Sea as seen by TIROS V. (TIROS photograph)

Moving now halfway around the world, Figure 1-8 shows Sakhalin Island, the northwest tip of the Japanese Island of Hokkaido, and clouds over the Sea of Okhotsk.

South of the equator, over Australia, TIROS sees such landmarks as Shark Bay and North West Cape, as in Figure 1-9.

Traveling northwest again to Eurasia, Figure 1-10 shows the Caspian Sea with the shallow salt-saturated Zaliv Kara-Bogaz opposite Baku (just east-south east of + mark) and the mouth of the Volga River at the northwest end.

And back again to the United States, Figure 1-11 shows Cape Cod and Long Island with the spiral cloud bands of a storm system off the coast.

Fig. 1-11. Cape Cod and Long Island with a major storm system to the southeast. (TIROS photograph)

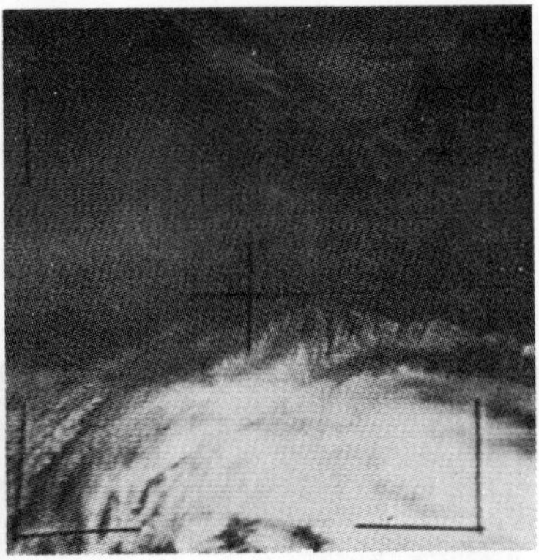

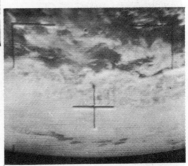

Fig. 1-12. The southern tip of Greenland as photographed by TIROS V. (TIROS photograph)

Fig. 1-13. Edge of polar ice and coastline of Antarctica. (TIROS photograph)

This world tour could continue indefinitely since the TIROS and Nimbus satellites have taken well over 300,000 pictures and there are few parts of the world and its major landmarks that have not been photographed. This is demonstrated by Figures 1-12 and 1-13. Figure 1-12 shows the southern tip of Greenland; the intricate pattern is formed by the ice cap and the fjords that cut into it. Other similar pictures on different days prove that we are seeing the ice cap itself and not a cloud formation. Figure 1-13 takes us to the other extreme, showing the edge of the Antarctic ice shelf and cloudiness offshore.

Another way to illustrate this coverage is by a typical map

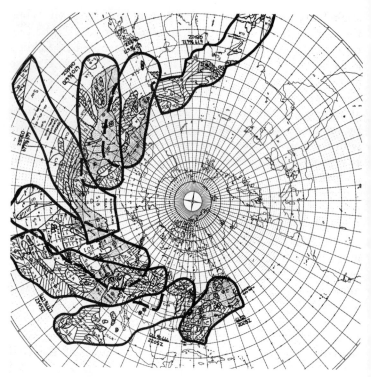

Fig. 1-14. Typical TIROS coverage in northern middle latitudes. (USWB)

of the areas photographed by TIROS on a single day. In this map, all of the areas within the heavy black boundaries were observed within a single twenty-four-hour period. The notations within the areas symbolize the cloud amounts, forms, types, and patterns that were seen; the way they are identified and used will be discussed later. For now, we will restrict our interest in this map to the extent of daily coverage it depicts. Figure 1-14 shows coverage on a typical day when TIROS was observing northern hemisphere mid-latitudes.

The satellite pictures shown so far were all taken by cameras with either wide or medium angle lenses. In these, the areas viewed measure about 750 miles on a side (for the wide angle lens) or about 450 miles on a side (for medium angle lens) when the satellite is looking straight down. When the camera views the earth at an angle, the area in the picture may be much larger. (This can be illustrated by holding a flashlight with a reasonably focused beam an inch or so above a world globe and comparing the area in the beam when pointed straight at the globe as against when pointed at an angle. When the beam is angled so that part of it shoots by the globe, the situation is comparable to a TIROS picture with the horizon showing, as in Figure 1-1.) When the earth is viewed at an angle, the distance along the horizon may be as great as 1500 miles. Pictures taken at an angle produce a distortion in the scale, with features near the horizon appearing smaller than they are when compared to those viewed vertically.

In TIROS I and II, one camera was equipped with a narrow angle lens which took pictures with greater visible details, but over areas only 1/100 the size of those covered by the wide angle cameras. In these pictures, the distance along each side is about 80 miles.

Figure 1-15 shows the comparative areas and details as seen by these two different types of lenses. The right picture, taken with the wide angle lens camera, shows much of the Gulf

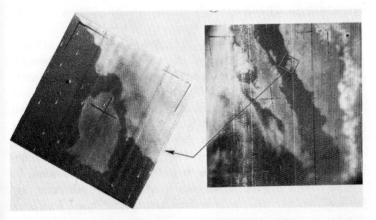

Fig. 1-15.   The Gulf of California and the island of Tiburon as seen by TIROS wide and narrow angle cameras. (NASA)

of California and the Baja California peninsula. The left picture, taken with the narrow angle lens, provides a detailed picture of a small portion of the Gulf, with Tiburon Island and the strait between it and the Mexican mainland clearly visible.

It is worth noting that the detail visible in the left picture cannot be obtained merely by enlarging the right picture. The resolution (the amount of detail that can be seen) in a television picture is limited by the number and width of the raster lines; these are the close parallel lines that can be detected in most TIROS pictures, and on the picture of a home TV set. Once we are close enough to the set to see these lines, we are seeing the maximum detail available in the picture. Moving closer will show us nothing more. And so it is with the satellite pictures.

In the TIROS pictures, this raster line limitation prevents seeing features smaller than about 2-3 miles in the wide angle pictures or smaller than about 0.2 mile in the narrow angle pictures. In Nimbus, the limitation is about 0.5 mile.

It is interesting to consider an unmanned spacecraft sent from some other planet and equipped with a TV camera comparable to the TIROS narrow angle camera. When it radioed its pictures home, what would the space scientists of Planet X deduce as to whether the earth was inhabited by intelligent creatures? Probably if this was their best source of information, they would see nothing to suggest the presence of man. Only a single TIROS picture is known to show a manmade feature, and it was taken under a far from common condition. Snow covered the ground and showed up cleared areas against the dark forest. A pattern of perpendicular lines appeared, caused by section line roads, cleared back to form fire breaks, spaced about 1½ miles apart. Actually, the cleared swaths are far narrower than they appear, but the light reflected from the snow was sufficiently intense to produce a bright response in the camera when the raster scan swept over it. At any one instant, the electron scanning beam in the TV camera integrates the light from the total area (about 0.2 × 0.2 mile for the narrow angle camera) the beam is viewing. Thus, a gen-

Fig. 1-16. TIROS I photograph of a great spiral storm in the North Atlantic on April 2, 1960. (TIROS photograph)

erally dark area with one small but very bright spot can show up in a picture the same as an area uniformly but only moderately bright. Basically, this is similar to the fact that sunlight reflected off a small mirror can be seen much farther away than the mirror itself.

Unless otherwise specified, the pictures shown henceforth will be from the TIROS or Nimbus wide or medium angle cameras, covering areas of the order of 500 miles or more on a side.

Before TIROS I had been in orbit a full day, it revealed cloud patterns whose existence, while suspected by some meteorologists, had never before been proven. These patterns were the spiral cloud formations associated with major cyclonic storm systems. The most striking early picture of such spirals, shown in Figure 1-16, was taken over the eastern North Atlantic on TIROS I's second day in orbit. (A detailed analysis of this storm is given in Reference 1-1.)

Prior to this time, spiral bands seen in radar pictures of hurricanes had led several meteorologists to suspect spiral cloud structures would exist in many whirling storms. But, even among these scientists, a doubt existed. Might it not be,

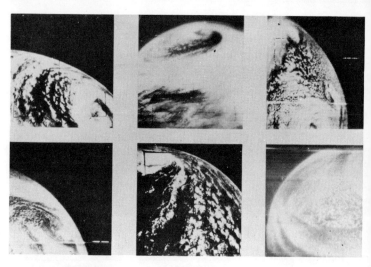

Fig. 1-17. TIROS cloud patterns. (NASA)

if the bands were there, that they were masked by other and more random clouds? This picture, and many others that came after it, ended these doubts. A few of the endless varieties assumed by these spirals are shown in Figure 1-17.

In succeeding months, as tropical hurricanes came under the eyes of TIROS, they too were found to have their own distinctive spiral patterns. Figure 1-18 shows typical views of the five 1961 North Atlantic hurricanes, all of which were observed by TIROS III.

While most people consider these spiral patterns to be the most fascinating of the many cloud formations seen by TIROS, the others deserve consideration. One familiar meteorological term is the cold front, which is the boundary between an advancing mass of cooler air and the warmer air it is displacing. As the heavier cold air pushes under the warm air, the cold air forces the warmer to rise, causing clouds to form along the front. A graphic picture of cold frontal cloudiness is shown in Figure 1-19, taken by TIROS I on its fifth orbit. A major storm covered the north central United States, with a cold front extending south along the Mississippi River (See Reference 1-2). The clouds associated with the storm are seen in

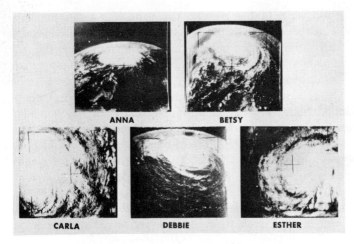

ANNA   BETSY

CARLA   DEBBIE   ESTHER

Fig. 1-18.   TIROS III hurricane pictures. (NASA)

Fig. 1-19.   A cold front along the Mississippi River. (TIROS photograph)

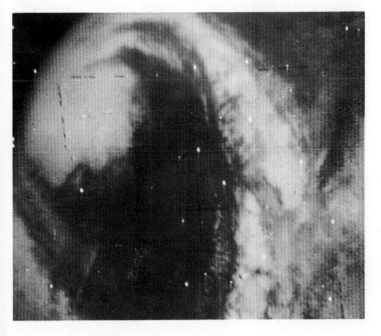

the top right of the picture; the band along the cold front runs out of it towards the lower left. Near the Gulf coast, the clouds again broaden out due to a warm front along the coast east of New Orleans and shower activity in the warm air over the Gulf of Mexico.

Often associated with severe cold fronts in the central United States are damaging hail and, fortunately somewhat less frequently, tornadoes—probably the most destructive of all weather phenomena. Hail and tornadoes are formed in severe thunderstorm clouds. On May 19, 1960, TIROS I photographed such clouds over the Texas-Oklahoma border west of Wichita Falls. The brightness of this cloud mass suggested that it was formed by towering cumulonimbus clouds. As this cloud mass moved north-eastward, tornadoes and hail broke out just southwest of Oklahoma City (See Reference 1-3).

Sometimes the skies clear rapidly behind a cold front. In other situations, particularly when cold air is moving south over warmer ocean waters, the air is warmed from below and stirred up, much like a pot of water boiling on a stove. This stirring is known as *convection,* and causes clouds to form where the air is rising. Such a case over the eastern Pacific Ocean is shown in the lower right picture in Figure 1-17, where cloud patterns due to this atmospheric convection cover the center of the picture. The cold front is out of the picture to the right or east; the storm can be partly seen in the extreme upper right corner of the picture. The dark, or cloud-free, area to the west is associated with high pressure moving in from the west.

When TIROS pictures are matched together for an entire orbit, or, where the data are available for a series of successive adjacent orbits, some extremely interesting large-scale patterns are often obvious. One of the first and most famous of these was constructed by Vincent Oliver of the U.S. Weather Bureau (See Reference 1-5), and is shown in Figure 1-20. Here, the top picture is a mosaic of unrectified TIROS photographs. (Unrectified means there was no adjustment to correct for the varying angles from which the camera viewed the earth.) In the lower picture, the cloud patterns have been rectified to

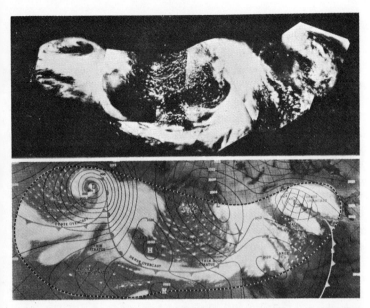

Fig. 1-20. Mosaic showing a family of storm systems extending from the mid-Pacific to the central United States. (USWB)

appear as they would if the camera looked straight down at all points. To aid comparison, the surface weather analysis has been superimposed, using isobars (lines of equal pressure) and the standard symbols for fronts. The correlation between the cloud patterns and the surface analysis is nearly perfect. Starting to the west, we see a major cyclonic storm near the International Date Line at 180° longitude. Running east from this storm is a cold front which extends to a second storm system along the west coast of North America. Patterns of broken convective clouds are seen to the north of the cold front and also behind a similar front extending west of the central Pacific cyclone. Another storm can be seen over the central United States. This complex family of weather systems extended a quarter of the way around the world, and has been shown to maintain its identity for a period of several days. It has frequently been said that: Nature uses clouds to draw its own weather map which satellites allow us to see.

Before concluding this preview of samples of the TIROS data, let us also look at two other phenomena noted in the pictures. One is sea ice, shown in Figure 1-21. These mosaics, based on pictures taken with the TIROS II narrow angle camera, extend from the tip of the Gaspe Peninsula (top left) across the Gulf of the St. Lawrence and Newfoundland into the Atlantic Ocean. In each of the top two strips, the frame at the right end duplicates that at the left end in the strip just below. In the top strip, we can see ice just off the Gaspe, open water south of Anticosti Island, and then broken ice again to a narrow strip of open water just west of Newfoundland. The middle strip features ice on the bays, rivers, and lakes of Newfoundland. In the bottom strip we see an unbroken ice shelf just east of Newfoundland, then open water with clouds above it.

The second phenomenon is snow on mountains, one example

Fig. 1-21.   A TIROS mosaic of sea ice in the Gulf of the St. Lawrence, and lake and river ice and snow over Newfoundland. (USWB)

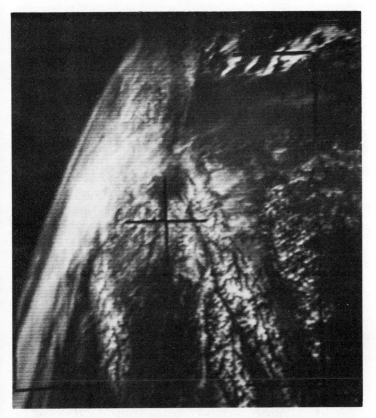

Fig. 1-22. Snow on the Canadian Rockies. (TIROS photograph)

of which was seen in Figure 1-4. Figure 1-22 shows a better
view of snow-covered mountain areas. The picture is of the
Canadian Rockies with the snow at the higher altitudes out-
lining the lower, snow-free, dark valleys.

The dozen or so satellite pictures we have so far examined
should leave little doubt as to the fascination of the views of
the earth and its weather that they provide. But the pictures
are not only fascinating; they are invaluable to studies and
applications of meteorology on a world-wide basis.

2

Meteorology—The Science of the Atmosphere

Many persons incorrectly think of meteorology and weather forecasting as synonymous. Weather forecasting is an important part of meteorology. Meteorology, on the other hand, is the whole science of the atmosphere. It is concerned as fully with the basic understanding of atmospheric conditions and processes as it is with the use of this knowledge for weather forecasting and other practical applications of the science. Progress toward better forecasting will continue to be limited by deficiencies in our basic understanding of the whole atmosphere.

Even if there were not the many pressing needs that presently exist for the practical applications of meteorology, the study of the atmosphere would be a legitimate and intriguing field of investigation.

From the viewpoint of basic science and its practical applications, there are few more complex and challenging scientific subjects than meteorology. Unlike many other scientific fields, we cannot isolate a portion of the atmosphere and subject it to rigorously controlled conditions in order to study it and conduct a desired precise experiment. Rather, meteorology must be based primarily on observation of conditions as they exist naturally, followed by deductions and tests of these deductions against other observations. This cycle must be repeated many times to satisfactorily determine one of the multitude of facts that remain to be established to increase our understanding. Only rarely can we effectively, let alone safely, influence a small aspect of atmospheric conditions in even a limited area. All attempts to model the atmosphere in a laboratory by a wind tunnel or a fluid tank of water have significant limitations.

To get some idea of what the meteorologist faces, consider a turbulent curving brook flowing over a series of rocks and boulders. Add an external source of disturbance, such as a gusty wind blowing over the brook surface. Then set as a task the learning of just what each individual thimbleful of water and every floating bit of debris in a 100-foot stretch of that brook is doing and why. In addition, there is the desire to be able to forecast where every thimbleful of water and speck of debris will be, several times each second, from the time it enters this 100-foot stretch until it leaves. In a small way, this is the task facing the science of meteorology, and the weather forecaster.

This analogy has its limitations, but there are these comparisons. The air, like the water of the brook, is a turbulent fluid. The curving of the brook brings in some of the effects of the curvature and rotation of the earth. The rocks and boulders simulate the roughness of the hills and mountains over which the atmosphere must flow. The gusty wind on the brook's surface may be likened to the effects of the sun's radiation and other influences from outer space. But we have been forced to ignore the fact that air can be easily compressed, while water is of a nearly constant density. And there are still many other aspects, which cannot be included by analogy, such as the condensation of water which creates much of our weather and serves as an internal source of energy.

The problem facing the meteorologist has been elegantly stated in the Agenda of a Weather Radar Symposium sponsored by the Raytheon Company in January 1963: "Take a large, almost round, rotating sphere 8000 miles in diameter. Surround it with a murky viscous atmosphere of gases mixed with water vapor. Tilt it back and forth with respect to a source of heat and light. Freeze it at the ends and toast it in the middle. Fill most of its surface with liquid that constantly feeds vapor into that atmosphere as the sphere tosses millions of gallons up and down to the ryhthmic pulling of a captive satellite. Then try to predict the conditions of that atmosphere over one small area 50 miles square for a period of one to three days in advance."

How does the meteorologist approach the problems he faces? One approach is through experience. He correlates what happens in similar cases; for example, it was long ago observed that storms often move approximately in the direction toward which the winds, at levels of 20,000-40,000 feet, blow. He applies more advanced statistical techniques to aid this empiricism by determining mathematically expressed relationships between sets of several observed conditions and the events that follow. But these approaches, while extremely useful now and probably for many years to come, are in a sense stop-gaps. Most powerful in the long run must be the use of the physical relationships that govern the atmosphere as they govern other phenomena. Based on such basic principles as Newton's Second Law of Motion, $F = MA$ (that is, force equals mass times acceleration), and the Conservation of Energy, we can, at least in principle, derive the equations that govern the motions of the atmosphere. At present, we find ourselves limited in this approach by three factors:

(1) Lack of adequate observations;

(2) Lack of knowledge of all the factors involved and how to express them in the equations;

(3) Equations too complex to solve even with the present high speed computers.

Accordingly, we try approximate and simplified forms of the equations, testing them against actual observations and then adjusting the approximations until they work fairly well. By such techniques numerical weather prediction, already in routine use, has been developed and is gradually being improved. (For a detailed treatment, see Thompson, P. D., "Numerical Weather Analysis and Prediction," New York: Macmillan, 1961). Even so, present techniques only forecast pressures, winds and some aspects of temperature, although as well as or better than a skilled human forecaster can. The human forecaster is still required to forecast the weather (such as cloud cover, precipitation, etc.) and the small-scale local conditions. To do this, he uses the results of the numerical prediction, observations, the other techniques discussed above, and his past experience (see Reference 2-1).

From the above discussion, it is evident that accurate weather observations are essential for meteorological progress, whether for attaining a better understanding of the atmosphere or for practical prediction of weather conditions for use in planning everyday human activities. It is, as noted in the next chapter, this continuing need for good observational data that creates the need for meterological satellites.

It is not the purpose of this book to provide a basic description and explanation of the atmosphere and meteorology. To do so requires a book in itself. But these are already available. Some of the good and readable volumes covering these topics are listed in the Bibliography at the end of this book, and an excellent "Selective Bibliography in Meteorology," including popular books and elementary texts, has been published in the August 1963 issue of *Weatherwise*.

3

Why Are Meteorological Satellites Needed?

"More data, more data,
From pole to equator—
Measure everything, everywhere
All of the time."

When Aaron Fleisher and Alan Bemis, meteorologists at the Massachusetts Institute of Technology, expressed these poetic sentiments at the banquet session of the Sixth Weather Radar Conference, their primary objective was to amuse.

Yet, like most humor, this poetic statement is only a slight exaggeration of the meteorologist's real and continuing need. Whether he is a research worker striving to understand the atmosphere or a duty forecaster attempting to predict tomorrow's weather, he must have measurements of a variety of meteorological parameters, over the entire world, from observing points reasonably close together and without excessive time intervals between the observations. The observing points should not be more than a few hundred miles apart and ideally should be less. The time intervals should not exceed twelve hours; six or even three-hour intervals would be far better.

Most people understand the need for a reasonable network of frequent observations in the areas for which forecasts are needed. But why, they ask, do we need observations all over the world? There are two answers. The first is that the entire atmosphere is a single, closely interacting mass of air. Disturbances arising in this single atmosphere may propagate throughout it, often as wave motions traveling faster than the winds. It is, for example, not uncommon for a storm to intensify in the western Pacific, with the accompanying formation of a deep trough of low pressure at altitudes of 20,000 to 40,000 feet, still over the western Pacific. But, just as waves on a water surface interact, the presence of this western Pacific trough may lead to formation of a second intense trough at an appropriate distance to the east, which usually places this second trough over North America and often leads to storm formation in the United States only a day or so after the initial storm intensification in the western Pacific. Accordingly, no experienced weather forecaster would attempt to predict conditions more than one or two days in advance (even for his local area) without consulting weather charts for the entire northern hemisphere. Ideally he should also know what is going on in the tropics and the southern hemisphere, but we lack sufficient data from these areas, and information on how they interact with northern hemisphere temperature zone weather. This is another challenge of the future.

A first reason for needing data from the entire world is for extended and long-range forecasts, even for purely local regions. This need encompasses data for the research that will lead to better long-range forecasting techniques as well as the data for making the forecasts.

The second need derives from the widespread nature of present human activities. Although some region may seem remote to us, to the forecaster there it is his local area for which he must have data for even short-range forecasts. The United States has projects in remote areas requiring meteorological support. Such projects include the Antarctic research program and its supply route between McMurdo and Australia; manned spacecraft recoveries in the tropical Atlantic and Pacific Oceans; rocket tests over a range extending down the South Atlantic to below the Cape of Good Hope and thence into portions of the Indian Ocean, and many others.

Let us accept, then, the need for global meteorological data. But what about the masses of observations we are already taking? Do we not have vast arrays of radiosonde stations, radar, weather reconnaissance aircraft, weather ships, and other observing systems?

Of course we have, but these more conventional systems are deficient in two ways:

(1) They are not appropriately spaced over the globe.

(2) There are certain types of observations they make inadequately or not at all.

With regard to appropriately spaced global coverage, consider the world radiosonde network, which is the most extensive of conventional, reasonably adequate, upper-air observing techniques. As Figure 3-1 shows, the very great majority of the stations are concentrated in the northern hemisphere temperate zone land areas of North America, Europe, and eastern Asia. The density of observations is far from adequate not only in the southern hemisphere, the tropics, and the Arctic, but also over most of the Northern Pacific. Because of this, locations of many storms over the North Pacific Ocean are often uncertain by several hundred miles. Even in the North Atlantic, the density of coverage is marginal.

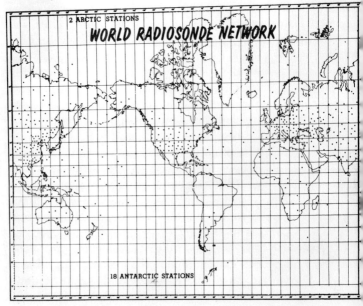

Fig. 3-1.   The world network of radiosonde observing stations.

To extend this network to at least marginal coverage for the entire world, even over land areas and where islands exist, there would be problems in remote regions of re-supply, communications, and sufficient trained personal willing to serve in such areas. But over much of the oceans, there are no islands in the right places. So we would have to use special weather ships. It has been estimated that for minimum weather ship coverage of just the North Pacific and the oceans of the southern hemisphere, annual additional costs would exceed $160 million. In contrast, it presently appears that we can, within a few years, maintain two Nimbus-type or other operational satellites aloft at all times, providing four-times-a-day coverage of the entire globe for an annual cost of less than $100 million. Obviously, economic factors favor the satellite approach. _Picture chart Fig 1-2_

There is still another reason for using satellites for meteorological observations. They provide data that can be obtained in no other reasonable way. Such data include the detailed cloud patterns associated with many different types of weather conditions and systems. In Chapter I we saw examples of these patterns, which were not known to exist prior to the TIROS. Examples include the spiral cloud patterns in whirling storms, convective cell patterns, and small scale eddies. The full information that can be deduced from these pattern details remains largely to be determined.

Without a satellite, these pattern details may be missed, resulting in inaccurate forecasts, even over areas of dense networks of conventional weather observations. Consider the case shown in Figure 3-2. The heavy cloud band in the TIROS picture is a solid squall line, with associated thunderstorms extending from upper Michigan into Kentucky. Before this picture was received, however, the thunderstorms, while observed, had been analyzed as only scattered, random, air mass showers rather than the continuous squall line which actually existed. An aircraft pilot, led by the forecast to believe he could dodge between scattered storms, would instead have been faced with flying through a continuous line of moderately severe weather.

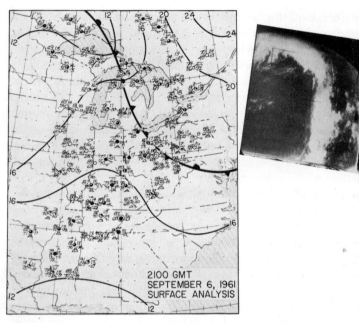

Fig. 3-2. A squall line over the midwestern United States, first detected from this TIROS picture. (USWB)

More significant to long-term meteorological progress will be a second type of observation for which the satellite is particularly suited. This is the observation of reflected solar and emitted infrared radiations. We will deal more fully with these observations and their significance in Chapter 6. For our present purposes, ~~consider that~~ the sun's radiation provides essentially all the energy which drives the atmosphere and produces our weather. We can liken this to the fuel put into an automobile. From ground-based measurements, we are already able to estimate accurately this incoming radiation at the top of the atmosphere, just as the gasoline coming out of the pump is metered. But a significant fraction of this solar radiation or energy is lost back to space immediately, due to reflection from clouds. We have had no good way to measure these reflection losses (known as the *albedo*) before satellites.

radiation

Uses badies bottle instead of car.

We can liken this lost energy to gasoline spilled when a tank overflows. Even if we know just what comes out of the pump, without measuring what was spilled we have no way of knowing just how much went into the tank. Similarly, although we know how much energy reaches the atmosphere from the sun, we must also measure that lost by reflection to calculate how much is retained. The meteorological satellite can do this.

At the other end of the atmospheric energy processes is long wave, infrared, or heat energy emitted to space. This we can liken to the exhaust of an automobile. In a very careful diagnosis of how well an engine is working, these gases will be analyzed and measured. Similarly, to understand fully atmospheric processes, we must measure the emitted outgoing radiation from the earth and its atmosphere and how this energy is distributed over the various infrared wavelengths. It was impractical to measure the outgoing infrared radiation, especially on any regular basis, until satellites could be used.

Because the observations were not available, most meteorological research and practically all forecasting techniques have been forced to ignore the energy inputs and losses of the atmosphere. In fact, most numerical weather predictions use adiabatic models, which assume no net loss or gain of energy. While there is no way to be sure, it is hoped that, with satellite radiation data available, we can take these energy gains and losses (and particularly just when and where they occur) into account with probable improvements in forecasting accuracy, especially in long-range forecasts. Of course, significant research with the radiation data must occur before the necessary techniques can be developed.

There is now little doubt that meteorological satellites are and will continue to be an essential addition to the observing techniques of the meteorologist. But it would be a mistake to assume that satellites will make all other methods of observation obsolete. This is far from the case. Satellites can do several things that other techniques can do only poorly, or at tremendous expense. On the other hand, there are vital measurements that, within the foreseeable future, satellites alone probably will remain unable to make adequately, if at all) Examples include pressure, winds, and detailed temperatures in the upper atmosphere. Figure 3-3 tabulates the author's analysis of the relative merits of satellites, as compared to weather reconnaissance aircraft, in observing various important parameters. Conventional measurements are invaluable in evaluating and calibrating what the satellite sees.

RELATIVE METEOROLOGICAL OBSERVATIONAL CAPABILITIES

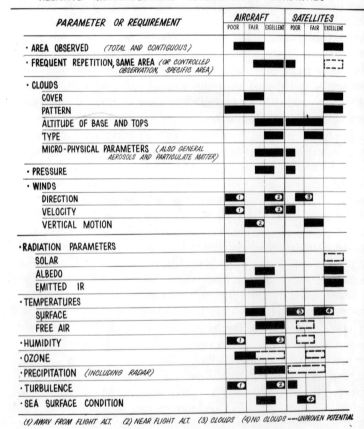

(1) AWAY FROM FLIGHT ALT.   (2) NEAR FLIGHT ALT.   (3) CLOUDS   (4) NO CLOUDS ----UNPROVEN POTENTIAL

Fig. 3-3. Comparison of the relative observing capabilities of meteorological satellites and weather reconnaissance aircraft. (NASA)

at end.

For many years to come, the optimum global observing complex for both research and forecasting will include a judicious combination of satellites, surface weather stations, radiosondes, weather reconnaissance aircraft, weather radar, weather ships in key locations, and probably still other techniques.

While meteorological satellites have revolutionized weather observing, they are only a step in the continuous improvement in the science and practice of meteorology. Satellites can only observe the weather, although they do an unequalled job of meeting some meteorological observing needs. But, by themselves, they can go no further. Only when observations are used by men, often aided by computers or other advanced devices, do analyses of existing weather or forecasts of future conditions result. There just is *not*, nor is it likely that there will ever be, a weather *forecasting* satellite. TIROS, Nimbus, and their successors are meteorological or weather-*observing* satellites.

4

The History and Background That Led to TIROS

Observations have been the foundation of meteorological progress. The history of meteorological observations has been primarily the expansion in both area and altitude of the observable regions of the atmosphere.

For most of his existence, man was limited to what he could see of the weather from horizon to horizon—an area normally well under one thousand square miles. In altitude, he was limited to what he could deduce from watching the clouds overhead and, until the middle 1940's and the advent of high altitude jet aircraft, even cirrus clouds were assumed to extend, except in rare cases, to altitudes no greater than 25,000 feet. Doubtless, early man noted the normal decrease in temperature and increase of wind when climbing mountains; quantitative measurements of these temperature decreases became possible when Galileo, in 1597, invented the thermometer.

Encouraged by the guidance and example of his teacher, Torricelli invented the barometer in 1643 and discovered the variations of pressure with time. Pascal discovered the decrease of pressure with altitude. Later, the invention of the balloon permitted measurements at moderate altitudes even away from mountainous areas.

The first man to deduce that storm systems lasted for moderate periods of time and traveled significant distances was Benjamin Franklin, who used as observations comments in correspondence from other parts of the colonies. In 1854, Napoleon suffered severe losses in a storm over the Black Sea and directed the astronomer Leverrier (also famous for his independent co-discovery of the planet Neptune) to investigate whether it might be possible to predict such storms.

Leverrier gathered observations from many parts of Europe for a period of several days before that Black Sea storm and demonstrated the validity of Franklin's deductions as to the time continuity and movement of storm systems. Synoptic meteorology (concurrent observations of weather conditions over broad areas) had begun, and on a research basis, weather horizons expanded to the order of one million square miles.

The establishment of telegraph networks soon permitted real-time use in daily forecasts of weather data from wide areas. Such a program, covering about the eastern half of the United States, was established by Prof. Cleveland Abbe, also originally an astronomer, shortly after the Civil War (see Reference 4-1). Gradually, the coverage was extended to the entire country, and the density of the network of stations increased.

Much later, a historical map analysis project conducted during World War II found it possible to construct reasonably accurate northern hemisphere surface analyses as far back as the early years of the twentieth century. But when Lindberg flew the Atlantic in 1927 and even during much of World War II, current analyses and forecasts over the oceans left much to be desired. By the last half of the 1940's, current northern hemisphere analyses had become barely possible, expanding weather horizons to nearly one hundred million square miles. Late in the 1940's, research post-analyses of the southern hemisphere as a whole began, raising the historical horizon for the first time to the entire 196 million square miles of the earth's surface. A pioneer in that program, Dr. Arnold Glaser of ARACON Geophysics Company, has since played a leading role in the meteorological satellite program. Even now, however, analyses of many tropical regions and large portions of the southern hemisphere remain grossly inadequate.

Other than limited manned balloon flights, progress in the vertical dimension was insignificant until a U. S. Weather Bureau network of box kite stations, begun in the late nineteenth century, provided data to altitudes of the order of ten thousand feet. Next came the development of instrumented unmanned sounding balloons which reached tens of thousands of feet. Although recovery of the instruments was necessary and so prevented use of the data for current forecasting, the Norwegians used these data during World War I to develop the air mass and frontal techniques of weather analysis, one of the most significant milestones of modern meteorology.

During the 1920's, soundings with instrumented aircraft (APOB's) provided limited upper air data for practical use in weather forecasting. Then, in the late 1920's and early 1930's, came a real breakthrough—the radiosonde. Expendable balloons, equipped to measure pressure, temperature, and humidity, and to radio back these data (and to obtain winds by radiotracking of the balloons' positions), permitted current use of upper air data over large areas. By the late 1940's, measurements reaching regularly to nearly 50,000 feet were available over most northern hemisphere land areas. (Currently, similar but better equipments often reach nearly 100,000 feet.)

Another field of technology, pioneered by Dr. Robert H. Goddard in the 1920's and 30's, developed by the late 1940's to a point where it could be applicable to meteorology. V-2 rockets, remaining from the German World War II development program (see Reference 4-2), were transported to the White Sands, New Mexico, Missile Range and used to investigate the upper atmosphere and the edge of space. To determine the attitude in space of the nose cone and other instruments, some rockets carried cameras to photograph the earth below, particularly the horizon.

One of the first meteorologists to grasp the significance of the clouds seen in these photographs, and probably the first to publish a discussion of the meteorological value of rocket photographs, was Major (now Brig. Gen.) D. L. Crowson of the U. S. Air Force (see Reference 4-3). In his historic paper, "Cloud Observations from Rockets" (January, 1949, *Bulletin of the American Meteorological Society*), Crowson suggested the use of television cameras in rockets so that the cloud data would be available immediately. He did not, however, make the key transition from the short-lived rocket observation to the long duration orbiting satellite. But his paper presented, for the first time, mosaics of cloud photographs taken from the outer edge of the atmosphere.

Probably somewhere in the long and amazing history of science fiction is the first discussion of the observation of clouds and weather from satellites. The first authoritative publication covering this subject was a scientific investigation conducted by S. M. Greenfield and W. W. Kellogg of the Rand Corporation. Because it was a small part of a secret Air Force study of the possible military uses of satellites, it was not generally available until republished in an unclassified version (see Reference 4-4), following the launch of TIROS I, in 1960. The first known public report proposing meteorological satellites was published by Dr. H. Wexler of the U. S. Weather Bureau in 1954 (see Reference 4-5).

Meanwhile, other rocket photographs of clouds were being obtained from time to time over White Sands. Finally, in October 1954, a major weather system was photographed on one of these flights. The spiral cloud bands of a high-level tropical storm moving in from the Gulf of Mexico were seen (Figure 4-1) which later dropped flooding rains on Chicago.

Fig. 4-1. Composite of photographs of a tropical storm taken from an Aerobee rocket over New Mexico, October 5, 1954. (U.S. NAVY)

This case has been analyzed by Hubert and Berg (see Reference 4-6). Based in part on these additional data, Wexler in 1957 published an updated and more detailed version of his earlier paper (see Reference 4-7). In it was a depiction of Wexler's conception of how typical cloud patterns over North America and nearby ocean areas would appear from a satellite orbiting at an altitude of 4000 miles (Figure 4-2). A comparison of the patterns in Figure 4-2 and TIROS I pictures obtained more than three years later demonstrated Wexler's remarkably astute foresight (see Reference 4-8).

The first year of the Space Age was ushered in by the launch on October 4, 1957 of the USSR's Sputnik I. But, by

Fig. 4-2.   Dr. Wexler's 1954 estimate of how a typical weather situation would appear from a satellite 4000 miles above Texas. (USWB)

this time, meteorological satellite research was moving aggressively forward in several different laboratories, and had been for several years. Although in some cases this work led to other projects, in most cases it had a definite influence on TIROS.

In New Jersey, the U. S. Army Signal Research and Development Laboratory (USASRDL) and its contractor, the Astro-Electronics Division of the Radio Corporation of America (RCA), were developing television cameras for use in space and considering compatible spacecraft configurations. To insure a spacecraft and its required launch vehicle would be matched, this program was closely coordinated with rocket developments underway at the Army Ballistic Missile Agency (ABMA) at Huntsville, Alabama; ABMA would soon be building the first satellite to be launched by the United States, Explorer I.

Concurrently USASRDL was developing the first partially successful meteorological satellite. As part of the IGY (International Geophysical Year) Vanguard project, it had been proposed that a simple spherical satellite with two optical scanners looking at opposed directions 45° to the spin axis could acquire data from which low resolution cloud cover maps could be produced (see Reference 4-G-3). The geometry was later to be applied to the TIROS scanning radiometer and will be explained more fully in Chapter 6. This satellite had been proposed by William Stroud and Dr. William Nordberg and was being developed by them and a team of colleagues including Drs. Rudolf Hanel and Rudolf Stampfl; all these scientists would later play key roles in TIROS. In concept, their spacecraft had many similarities to MOUSE (Minimum Observational Unmanned Satellite of Earth) (see Reference 4-9), a proposal of Dr. S. F. Singer (later Director of the United States Weather Bureau's National Weather Satellite Center).

The Stroud-Nordberg satellite was successfully placed in orbit on February 17, 1959, as Vanguard II. However, the severe weight limitations imposed by limitations of the Vanguard launch vehicle made it necessary to distribute the components in such a way that there was insufficient dynamic stability about the desired spin axis. As a consequence and probably due also to lack of a clean separation between the satellite and the third stage of the launch vehicle, the satellite wobbled in flight. Although adequate radio signals were received and the changes in brightness between cloud-covered and clear areas could be detected, the data points could not be geographically located due to the complicated scan pattern resulting from the wobble. Attempts to construct cloud maps from these data were dropped when the high quality TIROS I pictures made further effort unnecessary.

Although Vanguard II produced no meteorologically usable data, in retrospect it was far from a complete loss. The experience gained and lessons learned during its development and operation were very useful in the design and development of TIROS. Without this experience, it is improbable that TIROS could have been so immediately and fully successful.

Prof. Verner Suomi at the University of Wisconsin was also associated with the Vanguard IGY program. He was developing a small spacecraft to measure the energy lost to the earth and its atmosphere from reflected sunlight and from emitted outgoing heat radiation. Prof. Suomi's Vanguard satellite failed to orbit, but his similar experiment was incorporated in Explorer VII, launched October 13, 1959, and provided great quantities of valuable data (see Reference 4-10). Another version of the same basic experiment was later incorporated in TIROS III and subsequent TIROS satellites.

Work directed towards meteorological satellites was also underway prior to 1957 at the Geophysics Research Directorate (GRD) of the Air Force Cambridge Research Center (AFCRC) at Bedford, Mass. Emphasis was placed on ways to process, analyze, and utilize the data to be expected from such spacecraft. Early results of this research would be reported by the author and C. N. Touart before the end of 1957 (see Reference 4-11). GRD, in addition to its own in-house research, sponsored related study programs at such schools as Florida State University and the Imperial College of Science and Technology, London, England. Probably the most significant of this sponsored research was that conducted by Dr. Arnold H. Glaser, then of Blue Hill Observatory, Harvard University (see Reference 4-12). His now classic report presented the first quantitative analysis of the camera resolutions required to obtain various types of cloud information, and the radio bandwidths required to telemeter these data back to earth. It would play a significant role in the design of TIROS, as well as suggesting various advanced concepts for the analysis of meteorological satellite data, some of which still remain as topics for future research (see Chapter 14).

By 1957, development of a relatively complex meteorological satellite such as TIROS was possible. But, until Sputnik I was launched, the national will to support such an undertaking was lacking. The scientific soul-searching that followed Sputnik I led, among other things, to the establishment in the Department of Defense of the Advanced Research Projects Agency (ARPA). ARPA accelerated or initiated many of the United States space projects until NASA could be established.

During the spring of 1958, ARPA determined that a meteorological satellite would be an appropriate part of the U. S. space program and requested the three military services (Army, Navy, and Air Force) and the U. S. Weather Bureau to furnish their recommendations with regard to such a project. These various recommendations were presented and discussed at a historic meeting held in the Pentagon during the late spring. The chairman was Mr. Roger Warner of ARPA, who had present, among other consultants, Gordon Vaeth (now with the National Weather Satellite Center), and Dr. Michael Ference. Representing the Weather Bureau were its Chief, Dr. F. W. Reichelderfer; Dr. H. Wexler, Director of Research; and Dr. Sigmund Fritz, who would soon become chief of its Meteorological Satellite Laboratory. As they indicated, the Weather Bureau's prime interest was in the observations to be made and the study and use of the data.

The Army was represented by Dr. Ernst Stuhlinger of ABMA and several scientists and engineers from USASRDL. Dr. Charles Bates was among those present from the Navy. The Air Force, whose representatives included Maj. (now

Lt. Col.) Arthur W. Bostick and the author, proposed a complete system development program, including launch vehicle, spacecraft, data processing, and data use, built around a modification of its Discoverer satellites. Also present was Mr. Edgar M. Cortwright, representing the NACA which later that year would serve as the foundation for the establishment of NASA.

Before the meeting, Mr. Warner and his ARPA staff associates studied pertinent development programs and favored the use of the USASRDL-ABMA-RCA television camera development program as the keystone for a meteorological satellite project. But many details remained to be investigated, such as how many cameras should be used, what area should they cover and what amount of detail they should show, should there be radiation sensors, etc. Dr. Ference suggested and Mr. Warner agreed to the formation of an ARPA Committee on Meteorology to assist him in these matters. Dr. W. W. Kellogg of the RAND Corporation (a co-author of the first study in this field) agreed to act as chairman. The committee as initially formed included: Mr. E. M. Cortwright, NACA; Dr. E. Stuhlinger, ABMA; Dr. Charles Bates, USN; Dr. Sigmund Fritz, USWB; and Dr. William K. Widger, Jr., AFCRC. Later, many other scientists and engineers would serve with this group as the problems encountered required their assistance.

There would be little point in recounting here all the various changes in concept and design (see Reference 4-G-3) that this meteorological satellite went through before becoming TIROS. The final design will be described in detail in the next chapter. Just as examples, one side-looking camera was dropped, leaving only two of the originally proposed three. When the JUNO II launch vehicle development program was dropped, the Thor-Able was chosen in its place. A complex and sophisticated optical system for reducing and processing the pictures yielded to more straightforward, though less elegant, gridding techniques, described in Chapter 7.

Responsibilities for the program were centered in ARPA under Roger Warner, who was assisted by Dr. Kellogg. In April 1959, these responsibilities were transferred to NASA,

where they were assumed by Dr. Morris Tepper at the Headquarters level and Mr. William Stroud at the Goddard Space
Flight Center.

Spacecraft development was assigned to USASRDL, under
Mr. Herbert Butler, to be performed by its contractor, RCA-
AED, under Mr. Sidney Sternberg. Development of the
radiation sensing subsystem was assigned to Mr. Stroud at
USASRDL and transferred to NASA's GSFC when he and
his colleagues moved there. Launch vehicle responsibilities
were assumed by USAF, Space Technology Laboratories, and
Douglas Aircraft. Tracking and orbit computation were under
NASA. Data acquisition stations were under USASRDL and
USAF-Lockheed. Data reduction, processing, and utilization
was assigned to AFCRC, the Navy Photographic Interpretation Center, and the USWB.

After completion of the TIROS I operations, NASA was
able to reorganize more efficiently the program transferred
to it, and many of these responsibilities were reassigned as
regards TIROS II and later spacecraft of the series.

Before concluding this historical résumé, there are two other
important events that deserve mention. In December 1958,
some excellent cloud photographs were taken and recovered
off the east coast of the United States, using a Project Hugo
rocket. Although the weather situation did not provide information of great value as regards meteorological interpretation, these pictures were extremely valuable for developing
techniques which were used with TIROS data to locate the
points in such pictures and to compute latitude-longitude
grids.

About the same time, the Air Force started putting recover-
able motion picture cameras in a few missile nose cones being
tested from Cape Canaveral. Pictures from the first three, used
on Thor tests, were not particularly spectacular, but they did
provide information on certain sub-tropical cloud patterns.
On August 24, 1959, however, a spectacular and extremely
valuable set of pictures was obtained from an Atlas test.
Covering a large portion of the North Atlantic from the
equator to above 35° N latitude and east to nearly the coast

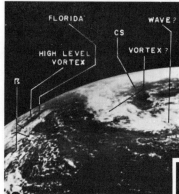

Fig. 4-3. View of Florida, a cold front over the Atlantic, and a wave on it, as seen from an Atlas rocket nose cone. (USAF, GE)

Fig. 4-4. View of tropical cloud bands and northeast South America, as seen from an Atlas rocket nose cone. (USAF, GE)

of Africa, during the period between separation from the rocket (shortly after launch) and the highest point of the flight east of Brazil, this film when projected gives some of the feeling an astronaut must experience as he views the earth. More significantly, these data were a great morale booster to the nascent satellite meteorologists by proving that important weather features—a front across the Atlantic off Cape Hatteras, an incipient small storm along it, major tropical cloud bands, etc.,—were not masked by random clouds but could be clearly seen in pictures similar to those to be expected from a satellite. Figures 4-3 and 4-4 show two of the several hundred pictures taken during this flight; in Figure 4-3 are shown a cold front over the North Atlantic with a nascent wave cyclone development on it. Figure 4-4 shows a view of major tropical cloud bands in the South Atlantic off northeastern South America. Figure 4-5 is a sketch in great detail, prepared by John Conover of AFCRL (see Reference 4-14), of all the cloud patterns for this entire area as filmed during this flight; it covers nearly ten million square miles, by far the greatest expanse of the earth (one-twentieth) ever seen at one time prior to the first TIROS flight. (In the figure, the clouds are sketched in black as contrasted to the normal white appearance.)

From these pictures, much progress toward the use and interpretation of satellite cloud pictures was possible; and they were a key factor in the immediate application of the TIROS data within three days of the first TIROS launch. Of greater import, deductions initially inspired by these pictures and confirmed by subsequent TIROS data later led Col. James Sadler to propose rather radical revisions to previously accepted theories of the large-scale wind patterns of the tropical atmosphere. (see Reference 4-15).

The passage of time and the sequence of the observational aspects of meteorological history has now brought us to the end of March 1960. TIROS I is about to be launched. Let us see what this satellite and its complex equipment looks like, what it does, and how it works.

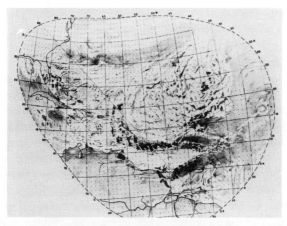

Fig. 4-5.   Sketch made by John H. Conover showing in detail cloud patterns seen from the Atlas rocket nose cone on August 24, 1959. (USAF)

5

TIROS—Its Equipment and How It Works

TIROS is shown in Figure 5-1 and schematically depicted in Figure 5-2. It is basically cylindrical in shape, about 42″ in diameter, and 19″ high (22″ with the projection of the camera lens below the base). The sides of the "cylinder" are 18 flat segments to aid in mounting the solar cells. Weight has varied from about 270 pounds for TIROS I to over 300 pounds as additional sensors and improvements were added in later TIROS satellites. A top view of the spacecraft, with the cover removed to show most of the equipment, is given in Figure 5-3a. Figure 5-3b shows Mr. William Stroud of NASA's GSFC pointing out the equipment to President Lyndon Johnson.

Fig. 5-1. TIROS (specifically TIROS III). (NASA)

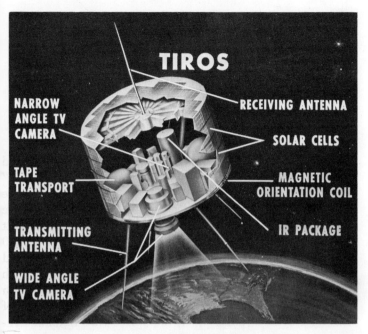

Fig. 5-2. A schematic cut-away view of TIROS. (NASA)

Basically, the spacecraft contains the following subsystems:

1. A structure, to hold the equipment.

2. Solar cells and storage batteries for power.

3. A stabilization subsystem, so the direction in which the sensors are looking can be determined.

4. Command devices and clocks to control the functions of the equipments and when they will be performed.

5. Beacon transmitters for tracking the satellite's position, and telemetry to provide data on how the various equipments are functioning.

6. Two cameras to take pictures of the earth's cloud cover, and tape recorders to store the pictures when out of range of a ground data acquisition station.

7. Radiometers to measure reflected solar and emitted infrared (or heat) radiation from the earth and its atmosphere.

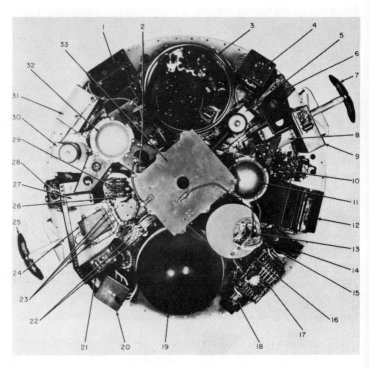

Fig. 5-3a. A top view of the TIROS spacecraft with the cover removed to show the equipment. (1) TV camera electronics package.
(2) TV transmitter power converter. (3) Tape recorder (cover removed). (4) Tape recorder electronics package. (5) TV camera. (6)
Tape recorder power converter. (7) Omnidirectional radiometer. (8)
TV camera control package. (9) Tape recorder power converter.
(10) Heat measuring equipment control panel and (below) command receivers. (11) Electronic clock. (12) Scanning radiometer.
(13) Heat measuring experiment electronics (and tape recorder)
package. (14) Horizon detector. (15) Nonscanning radiometer. (16)
Voltage regulators. (17) Battery protection panel and despin timer
(below) and TV transmitter (below). (18) TV transmitter power converter. (19) Tape recorder. (20) Tape recorder electronics package.
(21) Tape recorder power converter. (22) Main telemetry switches.
(23) Temperature sensors. (24) Omnidirectional radiometer electronics package. (25) Omnidirectional radiometer. (26) Beacon transmitters. (27) Auxiliary control package. (28) Voltage regulator. (29)
Attitude control switch. (30) TV camera. (31) Synchronous generator
and (below) TV transmitter. (32) Electronic clock. (33) Antenna
diplexer and (below) batteries. (NASA)

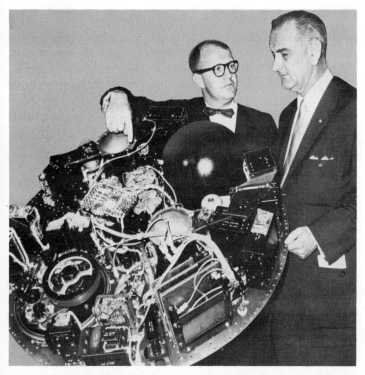

Fig. 5-3b. Mr. William Stroud of NASA's GSFC pointing out equipment to President Lyndon B. Johnson. (NASA)

8. Radio transmitters and antennae to relay the various data and information to the ground.

With the exception of the radiometers, each will be discussed in some detail in this chapter. (Since radiation measurement is a somewhat complex topic, it will be discussed separately in Chapter 6.) This chapter will also describe:

1. The procedures to test the spacecraft before launch so that it will have a very high probability of working properly in orbit.

2. The rockets and procedures used to launch the satellite.

3. The equipment and the procedures used on the ground for commanding the satellite and obtaining data.

The Structure of TIROS

The structure of a satellite must be designed to perform several functions. It must be able to support the various equipments and hold them in place under several conditions: (1) During fabrication, testing, and transportation prior to launch; (2) during the extreme shocks, accelerations, and vibrations produced by the rocket during launch; and (3) under the weightless conditions of space. Such support must be extremely firm and precise; the various devices must, of course, not bump against each other. For meteorological satellites, the cameras and radiation sensors, which are very carefully aimed, must have the same fields of view when in orbit if the users of the data are to be able to determine the areas being observed.

Satellite structures must not naturally vibrate at those frequencies where vibrations produced by the launching rocket are strong. Otherwise, those vibrations would shake the equipment in the satellite beyond its design limits. This is avoided by design, testing, and any necessary modifications.

The structure must distribute heat from various sources—particularly the sun's radiation and the various pieces of electronic equipment—to the cooler parts of the spacecraft (such as those not directly exposed to the sun) so that no part of the satellite becomes excessively hot or cold. The structure is aided in this function by properly coating the outside of the satellite so that it absorbs or emits radiant energy as may best maintain the proper temperatures.

These functions of firm support, resistance to shock and vibration, and distribution of heat must also be performed by the structural parts of each satellite subsystem and component.

The structure must have a means for clamping the satellite firmly to the launching rocket, and for cleanly separating the spacecraft after injection into orbit.

The structure of the TIROS base plate (see Reference 5-1) is shown in Figure 5-4. The base plate is strengthened by a series of ribs which tie together for still greater strength. Most of the equipment is attached directly to the radial ribs. The

Fig. 5-4. A view from below of a TIROS base-plate and its rib and ring structure. (NASA, RCA)

ring at the center clamps the satellite to the launching rocket. Even this structure was found to be inadequate and a number of brackets were added to tie the equipment together.

The structure must also be light because of the limitations of the launching rocket's power. For TIROS, an aluminum alloy was chosen.

The sides and top of TIROS support only a small fraction of the satellite equipment (solar cells, receiving antenna, sun sensor for north direction indication, and precession dampers) and are attached directly to the reinforced base plate. Nevertheless, to insure adequate strength, the top has a rib structure much like the base plate, and posts connect the top and base between each of the side panels.

When designing the structure, the shape and weight distribution of the satellite was considered. The data from Vanguard II were of little use because of its wobble. TIROS also spins in orbit and it must not wobble. Wobbling is prevented by having a mass distribution so that the *moment of inertia* about the desired spin axis is significantly greater than that about any other axis. (The moment of inertia is essentially the sum of the weight of each part of the satellite times its distance from the spin axis). This is why a toy top has its traditional shape and so spins longer before starting to wobble than, say, a pencil on its point. The desired distribution is one where most of the equipment is concentrated in a relatively flat disk, perpendicular to the desired spin axis and spread out as far from this axis as possible. So TIROS is a relatively flat cylinder. The diameter—and so the spreading of mass away from the axis—was limited by the diameter of the launching rocket. TIROS has only insignificant wobble, due to this design along with other devices to aid it, which will be discussed under Stabilization and Control.

Power Supply

TIROS uses solar cells (which generate electricity from sunlight) as its primary power source. They are used directly to drive the satellite's equipment, and also to recharge a set of nickel-cadmium storage batteries. These batteries operate the satellite during the night-time portions of its orbit (when the solar cells are inactive) and during short periods of heavy power drain, such as during picture-taking and data transmission.

TIROS carries 9120 solar cells, mounted on the sides and top of the satellite, to power its equipment. (140 other cells are used only for information on how much power is being provided, but furnish no power to the equipment.) Each cell is 1 by 2 centimeters in size and has an initial efficiency of at least 7.5 per cent of the solar energy falling on it. The cells are assembled in shingles of five each, which are further combined into modules of eighty cells. The shingles are connected in an appropriate array of series and parallel circuits to provide the required voltage and amperage. Diodes, which are devices that will allow current to flow only in one direction, are provided at proper points so if some of the cells fail they will not cause a power drain.

TIROS carries 115 solar cell modules. Many separate connections go to the storage batteries, and through a by-pass circuit directly to the equipments, so that as much power as possible is available even if some of the solar cells fail. Here again, diodes provide protection.

Depending on the amount of sunlight, the solar cells supply between 0 and 37 volts. Under the best of attitude conditions, in full sunlight, power in excess of 25 watts can be supplied. Average power available and used is between 16 and 21 watts. Contrast this with the 75 to 100 watts used by most reading lamps and you have some idea of how precisely the various equipments have been designed.

The power from the solar cells can go directly to the various equipments (through a voltage regulator) or to the nickel-cadmium storage batteries. Three separate groups of batteries are provided, so a failure in one group will not destroy the usefulness of the entire satellite.

Nickel-cadmium batteries, like the storage battery in your car, deteriorate after a number of discharges and re-charges. The life can be prolonged if the batteries are only partially discharged—if, at all times, they remain charged to 85 per cent or more of their capacity. The use of the TIROS equipment is carefully programmed to avoid excessive discharge.

The storage batteries were one of the most troublesome items during the pre-launch testing of TIROS I. At times the solar cells produced considerable power but little equipment was operating to use it; the storage batteries would then charge rapidly and create excessive temperatures inside the sealed cases. The cases would bulge and break away from the structure which equalize temperatures between the batteries and the rest of the spacecraft. Later heating during subsequent recharge would cause the battery to fail. This was overcome in two ways:

1. By regulators, which measure internal pressures and temperatures and, above certain limits, reduce the charging rate to a trickle.

2. By crimping the battery cases, so that bulging would not cause the cells to pull away from the structure.

As a consequence, there has been no catastrophic battery failure in any TIROS, most of which have continued to work in orbit for periods of four months to over a year.

Most TIROS equipments use power directly from the solar cells or the batteries without further regulation than keeping the voltage below 33 volts. The clocks, however, require that the current be reduced to 13 volts ± one per cent while the TV cameras and some other subsystems require reduction to 24.5 volts ± one per cent. In general, battery voltages have been readily maintained in the desired range of 26 to 31 volts

Stabilization and Control

A meteorological satellite is of no value unless we know the areas it is viewing. This has already been discussed in connection with Vanguard II. We cannot rely on landmarks, because clouds may hide them, pictures may be obtained over ocean areas without landmarks, and radiation data are taken during the night when pictures are not being made. Landmarks are, however, extremely valuable for confirming locations obtained by other means.

Ideally, a meteorological satellite would always have its base parallel to the surface of the earth below. Nimbus, described in Chapter 10, is designed to attain this objective. But, when TIROS was being developed, there was no way to do this within the weight the launching rocket could place in orbit

The alternative to earth stabilization (keeping the base parallel to the surface of the earth) is space stabilization (keeping the axis pointing towards a fixed point in space). Any spinning object will act like a gyroscope and keep its spin axis pointed towards a fixed point in space. This, often referred to as spin stabilization, was chosen for TIROS. Certain departures from exact stabilization, not foreseen in the case of TIROS I, were later used to advantage in TIROS II and other TIROS satellites.

Spin stabilization obviously requires that the satellite be spinning. For TIROS, the third stage rocket, with satellite attached, is spun to about 120 rpm (by small side pointing rockets) just before separation from the second stage. This insures the proper attitude while the third stage is firing. Accordingly, the satellite is injected into orbit with a spin rate of about 120 rpm. If all has gone well during the launch (as it has for all TIROS satellites so far), the attitude of the satellite (direction of the spin axis) is that determined when planning the launching sequence.

A spin of 120 rpm is too fast; the pictures would be badly blurred. Also the radiation sensors, to be discussed in the next chapter, would sweep the earth too fast to obtain the data desired. So the spin rate must be decreased by about 90 per cent. This is done by a device called a "Yo-Yo." Two weights, attached to long wires wrapped around the base of the satellite, are released by a timer shortly after separation. As they unwind (and finally fly off into space), they carry off about 90 per cent of the satellite's angular momentum and slow down the spin rate, ideally to 12 rpm. The action is analogous to the way a spinning figure skater slows down by extending his arms. The end of the wire (opposite to the weight) is connected to the satellite only by a hook so it can fly off into space after fully unwrapping. Otherwise, the momentum would not be lost, and the weights might strike and damage the spacecraft. Figure 5-5 illustrates the action of the "Yo-Yo" mechanism.

The satellite in orbit spins at about 12 rpm and presumably with a fixed spin axis attitude. But it cannot continue this rate of spin indefinitely. The many electrical currents in the spacecraft decrease the spin rate, since their magnetic fields interact with the magnetic field of the earth, similar to friction. Over a period of months, the TIROS spin rate gradually decreases to about 9 rpm. A slower spin rate is undesirable, since the satellite might wobble, the radiation sensors would scan the earth slowly, compared to the speed of the spacecraft in its orbit, and there would be gaps between lines of data points. To overcome this decrease, TIROS has several pairs of small solid rockets, mounted on and pointing along the rim of the base (as can be seen in Figure 5-6). When a pair on opposite sides of the satellite is fired (simultaneously, for minimum disturbance in attitude), the spin increases by about 3 rpm. Firing is actuated by a command signal radioed from the ground and has been successfully accomplished as much as one year after launch, this in the case of TIROS VI. These rockets are also used to speed up the spin when the initial rate

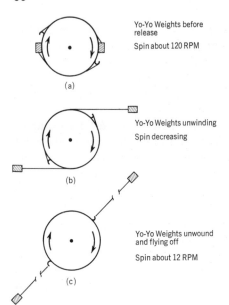

(a)

Yo-Yo Weights before release

Spin about 120 RPM

(b)

Yo-Yo Weights unwinding

Spin decreasing

(c)

Yo-Yo Weights unwound and flying off

Spin about 12 RPM

Fig. 5-5. Sketch of "Yo-Yo" despin action.

Fig. 5-6.   A view of two of the TIROS spin-up rockets attached below the baseplate. (NASA)

is slower than desired. Only a pair is fired at a time, so several cycles of spin decrease and speed-up are possible over the life of the satellite.

For accurate location of the weather data it is essential that any wobble be extremely small. This is achieved in three ways:

1. By a favorable weight distribution, as discussed earlier under the spacecraft structure.

2. By careful balancing of the satellite relative to its spin axis (much like automobile tire-wheel combinations are balanced) by a spin test and the precise addition of small weights as necessary. Of course, TIROS was built so only very small weights are necessary in the final test.

3. By a pair of small weights on rails along opposite sides of the satellite. These so-called TEAM (Tuned Energy Absorbing Mass) dampers are released during injection into orbit. These weights roll along the tracks, absorbing and damping the energy of any wobble. They are analogous to the shock absorbers on an automobile, smoothing out wobble as shock absorbers smooth out bumps. Their performance has been excellent; any TIROS wobble can be barely, if at all, detected in the most precise analysis of the pictures.

The next problem, assuming a stable spin, is to determine the direction of the spin axis, the direction the cameras are looking. (In some later TIROS the cameras point out the side; this is the Cartwheel configuration, discussed in Chapter 11.) Only by knowing this direction (plus the position of the satellite when each picture is taken) can the data be located. To accomplish this attitude determination TIROS is equipped with a horizon scanner. This scanner, looking out the side of the satellite, sweeps across the earth's horizon as seen from the satellite.

To describe this, it is necessary to anticipate facts that are explained in Chapter 6. First, the horizon sensor cannot respond to visible light, since we want to measure the horizon crossings and the attitude when the satellite is on the dark as well as on the sunlit side of the earth. An infrared detector responds to the temperature of an object regardless of whether it is in light or dark. In the infrared, outer space has a temperature of about 4°K (−452°F), while the earth's surface averages about 280°K (45°F) and even the coldest cloud tops are no lower than about 220°K (−63°F). (K is the abbreviation for Kelvin, a scale in which zero is −273°C.). Accordingly, in theory, a horizon would be sensed whenever the temperature measured by the horizon sensor changed between 4°K and anything above 220°K. In practice, it has turned out to be much more difficult. In the region of the infrared spectrum where the earth emits the most energy and where suitably sensitive detectors are available, the earth itself is seen where there are no clouds, but clouds are seen when they are there. It is often difficult to separate horizon crossings from the temperature differences measured between a clear area and an adjoining high, cold cloud top (see Reference 5-4). It might seem easy to separate a 220° temperature difference from a 60° temperature difference. However, the energy radiated, which is measured, varies as the difference of the fourth power of the temperatures. Therefore, the energy difference between the cold cloud (220°) and outer space (4°) is calculated as:

$$(220)^4 - (4)^4 = 24 \times 10^8 - 256 \approx 24 \times 10^8 \text{ (energy units)}$$

The energy difference between the surface (280°) and the cold cloud (220°) is:

$$(280)^4 - (220)^4 = (62 - 24) \times 10^8 = 38 \times 10^8 \text{ (energy units)}$$

The 60° temperature difference near 250°K represents a greater energy difference than 220° difference starting from near zero. Since the sensor responds to energy, it is difficult to distinguish horizons from cloud edges.

Assuming the problem of reliably detecting horizons has been solved (which it has been in part but not completely), how is this used to determine the attitude of the satellite?

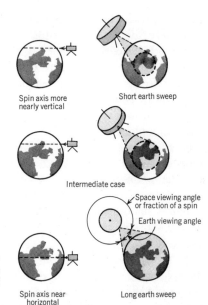

Spin axis more nearly vertical

Short earth sweep

Intermediate case

Space viewing angle or fraction of a spin

Earth viewing angle

Fig. 5-7. Relationship between TIROS spin axis attitude and the earth-space scan of the horizon sensor.

Spin axis near horizontal

Long earth sweep

Each time the satellite completes one spin (about every 5 seconds) a horizon will be sensed when going from space to earth, and a bit later another from earth back to space (Figure 5-7). (Of course, during that part of an orbit when the spin axis is pointed nearly straight down, there may be short periods when the horizon sensor does not see the earth at all.) Now measure the fraction of each spin that the horizon sensor is sweeping the earth. As can be seen from Figure 5-7, the greater this fraction, the less vertical the spin axis. Knowing the height of the satellite and this fraction, the angle between the spin axis and the vertical (the *Nadir angle*) can be calculated. One measurement gives the size of the nadir angle but not its direction. For example, with a single measurement, we might calculate a 45° nadir angle but not whether the spin axis was tilted north, east, south, or west relative to the point directly below the satellite. This can be determined, however, from the change of nadir angle (calculated from the horizon scanner readings) as the satellite moves around its orbit. If we calculate the minimum nadir angle during the orbit—and whether it is oriented left or right of the orbit—we can then calculate the attitude of TIROS at all other points in the orbit (see Reference 5-5). The amount of the minimum nadir angle is sometimes referred to as "NON"; the place it occurs in the orbit, given as time since the satellite crossed the equator going northward, is called "TOT."

Attitude measurements from the horizon scanner have not been completely satisfactory. Accordingly, they are supplemented by analyses of the pictures, using landmarks, and the angle between the axis of the camera and the horizon, which is usually the most accurate, by analysis of data from the radiation sensors, and by other methods. It is now seldom that the attitude of a TIROS is not accurately known within a very short period after launch and for the remainder of its useful life.

Knowing where the satellite is in space, and the attitude of its spin axis, provides all the information needed to locate geographically the center of a picture. However, we still need the north direction in the picture to locate the cloud features. In TIROS, this is done by reference to the sun. Nine sun sensors are equally spaced about the side of the satellite, each lying along a line of separation between side segments. Each sun sensor generates a pulse when it looks at the sun. From these pulses, the point on the edge of the satellite which was pointing toward the sun when a picture was taken is calculated. This determines where the sun is, relative to the top of the TV picture. Since the position of the satellite in space is known, as is the time when the picture was taken, the angle between north and the line from the sun to the satellite can be calculated from standard astronomical tables. Similarly, the angle (at the center of the area photographed) between north and the position of the sun at the time a picture is taken can be determined. It is then only a problem in three-dimensional geometry and trigonometry to determine north relative to the center of the picture.

In practice, the north indicator has not worked well because extraneous pulses, not readily told from those generated by the sun, creep into the system. In most cases, north is determined from landmarks (when visible) or from the horizons in the pictures as compared with the attitude and orbit of the spacecraft. For those pictures without horizons or landmarks, usually north can be extrapolated by matching similar cloud features from one overlapping picture to another, starting from one where north is known and going on to the others.

When TIROS I was launched, it was expected that the attitude of the satellite in space relative to the fixed stars would stay the same throughout its useful life. Analysis of the pictures soon showed this was not the case. The direction towards which the spin axis (and the cameras) pointed moved eastward in *right ascension* (the astronomical equivalent of longitude) at a rate of one and a quarter degrees daily. Furthermore, it oscillated south and north in declination (the astronomical equivalent of latitude) with a period of about 60 days and an average rate of one and a third degrees a day. Although this was entirely unexpected and complicated locating the positions of the clouds, it proved to be a fortunate effect. Before the launch of TIROS I, it was expected that due to the earth's motion around the sun and the precession of the plane of the satellite's orbit, some four weeks out of every ten the cameras would point only out to space on the sunlit side of the earth, and no pictures could be taken. The unexpected motion of the spin axis, however, kept the cameras pointing toward earth on the sunlit side. Pictures were possible every day, from launch on April 1, 1960, until a major electrical failure in mid-June ended the useful life.

Immediately after the spin axis wandering was noted, scientists at NASA's Goddard Space Flight Center and at RCA began an intensive analysis to determine its cause (see Reference 5-3). The cause was due to two factors:

1. To some degree, the decrease of the force of gravity with height, which causes an object in space to tend to align itself with the vertical.

2. Principally, interactions between the magnetic field of the satellite (caused by its many electrical currents) and that of the earth.

With the cause determined, it could be used to control

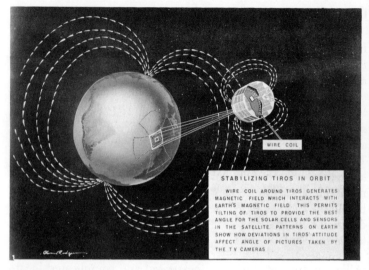

WIRE COIL

STABILIZING TIROS IN ORBIT

WIRE COIL AROUND TIROS GENERATES
MAGNETIC FIELD WHICH INTERACTS WITH
EARTH'S MAGNETIC FIELD. THIS PERMITS
TILTING OF TIROS TO PROVIDE THE BEST
ANGLE FOR THE SOLAR CELLS AND SENSORS
IN THE SATELLITE. PATTERNS ON EARTH
SHOW HOW DEVIATIONS IN TIROS' ATTITUDE
AFFECT ANGLE OF PICTURES TAKEN BY
THE T V CAMERAS.

Fig. 5-8. Interaction of the earth's magnetic field and the TIROS
magnetic attitude control coil. (NASA, RCA)

somewhat the attitude of future TIROS. TIROS II and each
subsequent TIROS have carried a Magnetic Orientation Control Coil, 250 turns of fine aluminum wire wrapped around
the base. By radio command from the ground, the current
flowing through this coil can be chosen from any one of
twelve settings.

Figure 5-8 illustrates the interaction between the magnetic
field of the satellite and the earth. Proper setting of the magnetic orientation coil moves the spin axis toward the best
direction for weather observations. However, the rate of movement can never exceed 25° per day and usually is less than
15° per day. The TV cameras are still useful only about one-
quarter each orbit. The control coil permits this one-quarter
to be over the area of best illumination. The coil also maxi-
mizes the length of the period of observation over the northern
hemisphere (where the needs of the United States weather
services are usually most pressing), and prevents the sun from
shining into and damaging the radiation sensors.

Command Devices and Clocks

We must be able to command which of the various TIROS functions are to take place, and when they are to occur. This is accomplished through its command subsystem and the associated camera clocks.

Commands are sent by special transmitters at each of the two Command and Data Acquisition (CDA) Stations. A special capability, usable only for starting the camera clocks, also exists at NASA's Minitrack Station at Santiago, Chile. The commands are picked up by the single rod antenna located on top of the satellite and sent to the two command receivers. Each receiver controls one camera chain and one, the various other satellite functions. Electronic equipments determine the nature of each command and cause it to be sent to the proper subsystem.

Commands are now sent at a precise frequency in the 148 Mcs band. The satellite identifies the function to be performed by the frequency of the audio tone (or combinations of tones received), and the length of time the tone persists.

The functions that can be commanded include:

1. Turn on and warm up the TV transmitters.

2. Take and transmit direct TV pictures.

3. Play-back (from the tape recorders) TV pictures taken remote from the station. The camera chain is also specified. Play-back of a camera can also cause the radiation data tape recorder to play-back simultaneously on those TIROS which carry radiation sensors.

4. Separately set each of the clocks which determine when and where remote TV pictures will be taken.

5. Start the clocks.

6. Temporarily shut off the beacon tones and transmit engineering telemetry on the condition of the various satellite equipments.

7. Permanently shut off the beacons, when the satellite is no longer useful. They can, however, be turned on again by the TV transmitter turn-on tone.

8. Change the setting of the magnetic orientation control coil.

9. Release the precession dampers and the "Yo-Yo" weights (if the automatic releases do not work). The same command tone is later used to fire pairs of spin-up rockets as needed.

In order that pictures can be taken when out of radio range of the CDA stations and precisely over the desired areas, clocks start the cameras. From the characteristics of the satellite's orbit, the time interval between a precise instant when within range of the CDA station and the later time when the camera will start viewing the desired area is computed. The clock is set to run for this interval.

Each clock is a precise electronic pulse counter which "Alarms" and starts its camera when it has counted 9,000 pulses. After being started, the clock counts at a rate of one-half a pulse per second (two seconds per pulse). Before being started, signals from the CDA station cause some of these 9,000 pulses to be counted very rapidly. The more pulses so counted before being started, the shorter time the clock will run before starting the camera.

For example, suppose the satellite is being programmed by the Wallops Island, Virginia, CDA station to take pictures near New Zealand. Assume that a convenient time for starting the clock over the CDA station is 9:34Z (Z stands for Universal, or Greenwich Meridian, time). The satellite will enter the New Zealand area at 10:42Z, or 68 minutes (4080 seconds) later. This time difference is established by the velocity of the satellite in its orbit. Therefore, the clock must run 4080 seconds (or 2040 pulses) after 9:34Z before alarming, if it is to alarm over New Zealand and take pictures there. For this to happen, 6960 pulses (9000 − 2040) must be put into the clock by signals from the CDA station before the clock was started, so that a total of 9000 will have been reached and cause the clock to alarm at 10:42Z.

Because the maximum number of pulses is 9000, a clock can run at the most five hours between being started and alarming. (This is somewhat analogous to regular alarm clocks, which cannot be set for more than about eleven hours' sleep.) Five hours equals about three orbits. There is a period, once each day, of slightly over six orbits between the last contact at the TIROS California CDA station and the next (first) contact at the Virginia station; these occur when the northern hemisphere half of the satellite's orbits pass only over the Pacific Ocean, Eurasia, and the eastern Atlantic Ocean. These limitations to coverage will be explained in Chapter 12. If only the regular CDA stations could command TIROS, pictures could not be taken on the last three of these orbits. To overcome this limitation, for TIROS III and subsequent TIROS, the Santiago, Chile, Minitrack station has been equipped to start clocks previously set by the California CDA station.

Tracking Beacons and Engineering Telemetry

A continuous radio signal is needed from a satellite in orbit so that tracking stations can determine its direction as it passes nearby; these data are used to determine the exact shape and inclination of the orbit, for predictions of the future positions and tracks of the satellite. These signals are also used to keep the large data acquisition antennae aimed directly at the satellite as they track it across the sky; this insures that command signals are beamed directly toward the satellite, and that the ground receivers can best receive the television and radiation data signals transmitted from TIROS.

To insure that these signals are available even if there is a partial failure, each TIROS carries two beacon transmitters. In the earlier TIROS they transmitted on frequencies near 108 Mc (megacycles or millions of cycles). The beacons now transmit at 136.23 and 136.92 Mc with a strength of 30 milliwatts (a milliwatt is one-thousandth of a watt).

So that the beacons will not keep transmitting after the spacecraft is no longer useful, they can be turned off by a ground station command. If this should happen accidentally, the beacons can be turned on again by the signals that turn on the TV transmitters. At times this also happens from random radio signals from the many always radiating from the earth. TIROS VI and subsequent TIROS are equipped with so-called "fail-safe" timers (precision electronic watches with independent power sources) which, one year after launch, are to cut off the beacon transmitters from the main TIROS electrical power system and so silence them permanently.

These shut-off systems prevent waste of the crowded radio spectrum, while providing reasonable assurance against a useful TIROS being lost. If a TIROS remains useful more than one year after launch, the TV transmitters can still be commanded and operated. This was actually done with TIROS VI which, ironically, was the first TIROS to operate successfully for over a year.

The beacon signals also carry two essential types of information. One is the earth edge crossings of horizon sensors, used to determine satellite attitudes.

The second type of data is called engineering or "housekeeping" telemetry. With a complex spacecraft like TIROS, it is not enough just to examine its sensor data to know how well the satellite is working. We need more precise information to (1) evaluate whether each system and subsystem is working as designed, (2) determine actions to take for best continued performance if everything is not just right, and (3) design improvements for use in later spacecraft of both the same and different types.

These data are analogous to such instruments in a car as the temperature gauge (or warning light), the "low oil pressure" light, the "no-charge" light, and fuel gauge. As long as all goes well, we hardly notice these indicators and drive on our way, but when the gas is low (or the fan belt breaks and the temperature rises above safe limits), they warn us to take the actions that prevent permanent damage.

The TIROS engineering telemetry provides some forty different pieces of data on how well the satellite is operating to the ground stations, on command, each time the spacecraft passes overhead.

One very essential use of these data is to calculate, from solar cell and current regulator voltages, the state of the battery charges. From this, it is decided how many cloud pictures it is safe to program each day without unduly discharging the batteries.

One example of the diagnostic use of the housekeeping telemetry was for TIROS V; when one camera failed, it was determined to be a malfunction in the filament circuit and not one of the many other circuits. Studies to develop better filament circuits and components were immediately begun. Many of the improvements in the later TIROS, and in Nimbus, have resulted from TIROS engineering telemetry data.

Television Cameras and Tape Recorders

The primary purpose of TIROS is, of course, to observe meteorological conditions on the earth below. All TIROS have done this, at least in part, by television cameras, which provided the cloud pictures shown earlier. Equally important in the long run, but less spectacular, are the radiation data which will be discussed in the next chapter. Since not all TIROS carry radiation sensors, we can consider the TV cameras as the heart of the satellite.

The TIROS TV cameras are in some ways similar to the studio cameras which provide the pictures shown by your home television. But there are some important differences.

Perhaps the most important difference between TIROS and ordinary television is that the TIROS cameras operate as still-picture, slow-scan devices, while the cameras which send pictures to your home TV are of a motion-picture, rapid scan type. TIROS cameras make snapshots while commercial TV cameras make movies. The TIROS cameras cannot take pictures faster than one every two seconds (actually they are never taken more often than once every ten seconds), while commercial TV operates at a rate of thirty pictures per second.

The second difference is the inner electronic workings of the TV camera tubes. TIROS uses a *vidicon* type of camera; commercial TV uses almost exclusively the image-orthicon. The reason is that, while image orthicons can operate with less illumination, at present they are heavier, and cannot reliably stand the shocks and vibrations associated with a satellite launch. (Image orthicon cameras may be used in later meteorological satellites to take cloud pictures by moonlight and, just possibly, by only the illumination of starlight; see Chapter 14).

Vidicon cameras can be made small (the tube itself in TIROS is only a bit over one-half inch in diameter and, even with its immediate exterior electronics, is only about the size of a water glass), light (as low as four and one-half pounds, including optics), and rugged to meet the launch environment. In Figure 5-9, the camera and its immediate electronics occupy only the light grey cylinder at its far right. The attached cylinder is the special wide angle lens. The small black tube is the magnetic shutter mechanism, and the rectangular boxes contain additional electronics associated with the camera. Figure 5-10 shows the actual size of the vidicon tube itself.

Vidicon camera operation is shown schematically in Figure 5-11. A shutter is opened for only 1.5 milliseconds (0.0015 seconds), and the cloud scene is focused on the transparent electrode. This electrode, an efficient current conductor, is extremely thin. The light focused on it easily passes through to the photoconductive layer on its rear. The photoconductive

Fig. 5-9.   A TIROS TV camera and its associated electronics package. (NASA)

Fig. 5-10. The TIROS vidicon tube, showing its miniature size. (RCA)

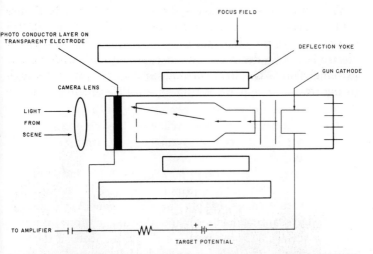

Fig. 5-11. Diagrammatic representation of the vidicon used in TIROS TV cameras. (NASA)

material, a good electrical insulator when dark, becomes a good conductor when exposed to light. Before the shutter is opened, it is "primed" (in the dark) by an electron beam. This deposits a uniform layer of electrons (negative charges) on its rear surface. The transparent electrode has a fixed positive charge. When an image falls on the photoconductive layer, its electrons leak to the conductor in bright areas (and in proportion to the brightness). In the dark areas, the electrons remain. This pattern of charge can be stored on the photoconductive layer for several seconds, allowing the picture to be scanned slowly. In TIROS, this scanning takes two seconds.

The scanning electron beam, from the gun cathode, is focused and caused to scan the image (line by line) by focus and deflection coils; this is the same as for an image orthicon (see Reference 5-7). These coils are much the same as in the picture tube of your home TV. The electron beam is attracted to the positively charged electrode. Where the image was dark, the beam is repelled by electrons on the photoconductive layer and no current gets to the electrode. In the lighter portions of the picture, there are fewer electrons; the beam electrons get through in proportion to the brightness of the scene. At the electrode, they cause a current proportional to the scene brightness. This current is amplified and its signals are immediately (or after storage in the tape recorder) transmitted to the ground. There they form the picture, as in your home television, but at a slower rate.

After the picture has been scanned, the photoconductive layer is "flooded" to remove remaining electrons, reprimed, and can then take another picture.

To summarize the vidicon operation in less detail: (1) the sensitive surface in the vidicon is prepared to receive and store the picture image; (2) the shutter is momentarily opened (as in any snapshot camera) and the image stored on this sensitive surface; (3) the image is slowly scanned off the surface, creating a signal that is radioed to the ground and used there to recreate the picture; and (4) the surface is erased and prepared for the next cycle.

This snapshot, still-picture, slow scanning operation is used because the cloud patterns change too slowly to justify motion picture type operation. The snapshots are taken just frequently enough to provide some overlap from one picture to the next. Furthermore, and equally vital, the pictures can be transmitted in some 30 kilocycles (thousands of cycles) of radio bandwidth (only about 3 times that of ordinary commercial radio) whereas motion picture TV would require at least 4 megacycles (millions of cycles)—commercial TV uses 6 megacycles for each channel. Such wideband transmission would require far more power and sophisticated components than the size and weight of TIROS would permit.

Before following the TV picture signal after it leaves the camera, there are a few other aspects of the cameras worthy of mention. All TIROS cameras are scanned at 500 lines per picture (in commercial TV, 525 lines are used in the United States). The corresponding width of a line in the pictures taken, as compared to a distance on the ground, of course depends on the lens used and the angle of view, as discussed in Chapter 1. The light entering the vidicon is filtered to be principally in the red end of the visible spectrum and a portion of the near-infrared spectrum; this avoids short wave length (blue) light, where haze might cause a picture clarity problem, while staying within wavelengths to which the sensitive surface of the vidicon is responsive. The lens apertures are chosen to optimize exposure of sunlit clouds.

The reference marks in the picture (the + at the center and the four L-shaped marks, one near each corner) are etched directly on the vidicon surface. They retain a fixed relation to the lens and are used to locate objects relative to the center of the picture. Any changes in their positions indicate distortions introduced by the camera electronics or other portions of the data transmission, and presentation chain.

When operating in the direct mode within the radius of reception of a ground station (by-passing the tape recorder), pictures can be taken either once every ten seconds or once every 30 seconds, at the option of the station operators. When in the remote mode (tape recorder storage of the pictures), after the sequence is started by the clock, pictures are taken once every 30 seconds for a total of 32 for any one camera, after which the camera is shut off automatically.

After the picture signals leave the vidicon, they are amplified and used to FM (frequency modulate) an 85 Kc subcarrier. In frequency modulation (FM), the instantaneous strength (voltage) of the input signal controls the instantaneous frequency of the output signal. If the satellite is over a ground station, this modulated subcarrier is then applied in the two-watt transmitter to frequency modulate a radio carrier frequency at 235 Mc.

Away from a ground station, the modulated subcarrier goes to a tape recorder specially developed by RCA for TIROS. During a picture-taking cycle, the recorder turns and records only when a picture is being scanned off the vidicon; between it is stopped to avoid wasting tape. When playback is commanded over a data acquisition station, the tape reverses (the last picture is read-out first) and plays back without pauses at the same 50 inches per second rate used during recording. The 400 feet of ⅜-inch Mylar-base tape take 32 pictures.

Each TIROS TV camera system chain is virtually independent, having its own clock, camera, recorder, and transmitter. The value of this independent duplication, or redundancy, has been demonstrated by TIROS III, V, and VI; each operated successfully for several months, providing great quantities of valuable data, after one camera had ceased to function.

In TIROS VIII, a special automatic picture transmission (APT) camera, developed for use in Nimbus and described in Chapter 10, replaced one of the regular TIROS cameras in order to permit testing of this new APT system.

Transmitters and Antennae

TIROS has several types of information to radio to the ground. The steady tracking beacon signals, the horizon information modulated on them, and the engineering telemetry data, are transmitted over two independent 30-milliwatt transmitters. The TV picture data are transmitted by two independent two-watt FM transmitters. They use the same frequency since, if both are used on a single pass, they are operated sequentially. The radiation sensor data (to be described in the next chapter) are transmitted over a single transmitter operating at 237.8 Mc; it transmits on the same command as, and in parallel with, one of the two TV transmitters.

These transmitters all use a common antenna system, the four rods mounted on the base of the spacecraft. (The single rod antenna at the top only receives command signals.) This single antenna system is connected to the several transmitters through a diplexing network which prevents "cross-talk" or interference between the different signals.

Qualification Testing

To insure that a satellite will operate properly in orbit, it must not only be well designed; it must be thoroughly tested.

Testing starts right at the design stage through the choice, wherever possible, of components that have already been tested and so have proven their capability. Then, as the components are manufactured and assembled into subsystems, the highest possible standards of quality control and inspection are rigidly enforced.

At each stage of component manufacture and assembly, all tests of the types to which the finally-assembled satellite will be subjected are conducted. This repeated testing locates inadequate or defective materials and workmanship as early as possible, when they can be corrected with minimum delays and expense.

Testing is conducted at three levels. The first, *preprototype,* demonstrates that, under normal conditions, the unit will perform as designed. Preprototype testing is usually applied to so-called "bread-board" units, which are electronically identical to the final device but are seldom constructed to survive the rigors of launch and space.

The most extreme testing is at the *prototype* level. A spacecraft, identical in all respects to that actually to be flown, is subjected to a series of comparatively severe shock and acceleration, vibration, thermal vacuum, and other tests. Each test subjects the prototype spacecraft to approximately three times the stress expected on an actual flight. Should any inadequate design or performance be noted, or a malfunction or failure occur, the test is stopped; the defect corrected. In some cases, a major redesign is required, as for the TIROS storage batteries. The test is then completely recycled until at least one testing cycle is completed with successful performance at all times. Prototype testing insures that the design and components have a margin of safety sufficient to protect against the random variations inevitably encountered between separate but presumably identical materials, components, and assemblies. The prototype is not intended to be flown; it serves its purpose by undergoing and ultimately withstanding tests at a significantly higher level than are expected to be encountered in actual flight. The strains it has encountered are sufficient to make it unwise to actually launch it except in an emergency situation.

Each spacecraft to be launched is put through similar tests, but only at the levels expected to be encountered in flight. Again, any malfunction will cause the test to be stopped, the defect corrected, and the test completely recycled. The objective is to catch any defects in the individual components used or in the workmanship during their assembly into the final spacecraft.

TIROS has gone through many vital tests in achieving its unusually high level of success. First, functional tests, to show each unit could do the things it was supposed to, were performed. These included electrical tests and operation of each piece of equipment in the assembled satellite to be sure, not only that it performs properly, but that it does not interfere with other units (for example, to be sure that signals generated by the TV cameras are not leaking into the radiation sensor circuits).

Other special tests have included operation of the "Yo-Yo" system to measure the degree of spin deceleration, antenna pattern measurements to insure the radio signals to and from the satellite could be received at any spacecraft attitude relative to the data acquisition antennas, solar cell efficiency tests, and mechanical testing of the strength of the structure.

Environmental qualification tests at both prototype and flight levels have included:

1. Shock and acceleration, to insure the satellite would operate after launch. Acceleration tests were conducted on

a large rotating boom, similar to that used for astronaut training, with all satellite equipment in the status it would be during an actual launch.

2. Vibration, again to simulate conditions encountered during launch.

3. Thermal vacuum. Where the two previous tests concern the launching environment, this test simulates conditions after the satellite is placed in orbit. The spacecraft is placed in a chamber which is evacuated to as near space conditions as the pumping equipment permits. Vacuums of the order of 10^{-5} mm of mercury (one ten-millionth of normal pressure at the earth's surface, 760 mm of mercury) are used. During this test, contact with the satellite is only by radio links and the satellite is operated, as closely as possible, as in space. The solar cells are illuminated, to provide power, in light-dark cycles simulating the orbit around the earth. The temperature is varied between 0°C and 50°C. The cameras and other sensors view suitable targets, and are read out to insure the data quality meets specifications.

After all tests are successfully completed, alignment is rechecked. After a final functional check of the electronic systems, the spacecraft is finally ready for shipment to the Atlantic Missile Range, Cape Kennedy, Florida.

Launch Vehicles, and Launching Procedures and Events

TIROS I was launched with a Thor-Able; the remaining TIROS have used the Thor-Delta (sometimes referred to merely as the Delta) for launch. Since the Thor-Delta is an improved version of the Thor-Able, only the Delta will be discussed here.

The Thor-Delta is a three-stage rocket standing some 92 feet high and weighing, fully fueled, about 112,000 pounds. Figure 5-12 shows a Thor-Delta without the protective "shroud" over the spacecraft. The comparative size of the spacecraft (TIROS II) and the rocket required to place it in orbit is, to say the least, striking.

Fig. 5-12. TIROS II on its launch vehicle before the shroud was put in place. (NASA)

A TIROS launching starts three weeks before the actual launch date with erection and check-out of the Thor first stage, followed by the mating and check-out of the second stage. A week before the end of this period, the spacecraft is mated to the third stage and the combined third-stage-spacecraft spin-balanced to insure against wobble during third stage burning and injection into orbit. A few days before launch, the third stage and then the spacecraft are mounted on the launch vehicle and further checks of the entire complex are begun. Particularly important are RFI (radio frequency interference) checks to insure radio transmissions to or from one part of the rocket-spacecraft system do not interfere with those to or from another. During all checks, after mounting on the launching vehicle, the spacecraft is operated purely by radio links.

The final countdown begins in the evening, at a precise time aimed at launch occurring shortly before sunrise. Permissible launch times are limited to a "window" lasting only about an hour if the radiation sensors are carried, and not over three hours without them. This is so the satellite will enter its orbit with a proper attitude to the sun to optimize (1) illumination of the areas that can be photographed, (2) the power provided by the solar cells, and (3) prevention of the sun shining directly into the scanning radiation sensors. To understand a part of this requirement—illumination of the areas to be photographed—consider that the satellite is injected into orbit over the North Atlantic with its spin axis parallel to the earth and the cameras looking back along the orbit. Since the spin axis stays fixed in space at least for short periods of time, one-quarter orbit later the spin axis and the cameras are looking essentially straight down. This occurs over Arabia and, purely by coincidence, near the holy Moslem city of Mecca. Because of this vertical view of this area early in the life of the satellite, many excellent pictures of the Red Sea and its vicinity have been obtained. This is the area, on the first orbit, where maximum illumination, or local noon, is desired. Local noon in Arabia is about 4 AM over the eastern United States.

In theory, a TIROS could be launched at any hour and slowly swung into the proper attitude using the magnetic control coil. But this would make successful operation of the spacecraft entirely dependent on the magnetic coil. Since this is an unnecessary risk, launch is made when the satellite will automatically assume the correct attitude. As TIROS I showed, even without a magnetic control coil, a TIROS so launched can provide valuable data for at least several months.

With the time of launch so limited, provision for correcting trouble during the final countdown must be made. This is done by scheduling a one hour "built-in hold," an hour available to catch up with any time lost.

During the final countdown, every subsystem of the launch vehicle, the spacecraft, the command and data acquisition stations, and the worldwide tracking stations and their communications are again checked. Any significant weakness will cause the launch to be delayed until it is corrected; if necessary, the launch will be postponed to the next day. Since there is no way to correct defects after launch, the slightest malfunction in the satellite or launch vehicle will delay launch until corrected.

Fig. 5-13.   The TIROS
launch.   (NASA)

Suppose we join a TIROS countdown at T minus 35 (T 35) minutes, just as the "built-in hold" ends. The Delta stand: fueled except for its lox (liquid oxygen); as far as can be told, it and the spacecraft are ready to go. The count is picked up, the lox is added and then the pad is cleared of all person nel. Then final checks of the satellite and crucial launch vehicle systems are run. These include guidance gyros, the C-band radio beacon used to track the vehicle during launch, the slewing (moving to control flight direction) of the engine, and several dozen others. Finally, as T minus zero approaches, the lox ports are closed and, if all goes well, we are ready for launch. A launch without a few minutes of "holds" during the final minutes is rare. In several cases, accumulated holds have led to launch only a very few minutes before the end of the permissible window.

We will assume that all goes well, this time, however, and a few seconds before T-0 the engine is ignited. A quick check by special automatic devices shows all is well; the clamps holding the vehicle to the pad are released; the umbilical tower (providing last minute electrical connections) discon nects and swings away; and the launch vehicle "lifts-off." It

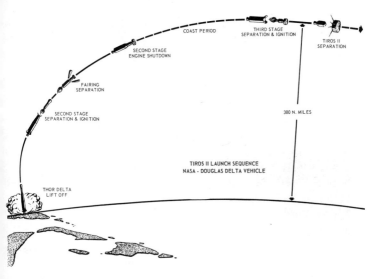

COAST PERIOD

THIRD STAGE
SEPARATION & IGNITION

TIROS II
SEPARATION

SECOND STAGE
ENGINE SHUTDOWN

FAIRING
SEPARATION

SECOND STAGE
SEPARATION & IGNITION

380 N. MILES

TIROS II LAUNCH SEQUENCE
NASA - DOUGLAS DELTA VEHICLE

THOR DELTA
LIFT OFF

Fig. 5-14.   The TIROS launch and injection sequence. (NASA)

rises slowly, but with ever-increasing speed. Figure 5-13 shows
TIROS I a split second after lift-off.

At first the rocket goes straight up, but soon it "rolls" about
its vertical axis, to the proper orientation for the northeast
trajectory used in a TIROS launch. About ten seconds after
launch, it starts to pitch (turn slowly towards a more horizontal position) and starts out over the ocean as it continues
to gain altitude. The launching sequence, described below,
can be followed in Figure 5-14. The Thor engine burns for
just under three minutes, after which it is shut-down, the
second stage engine ignited, the two stages separated, and
slightly more than three minutes after launch, the shroud
covering the satellite is blown off, exposing TIROS to space.

The second stage engine burns until slightly more than four
minutes after launch. After this, the second stage, with the
third stage and the satellite still attached, coasts upward
(under the guidance of the BTL (Bell Telephone Laboratory)
guidance system to maintain proper attitude) until, something
more than ten minutes after launch, they reach orbit altitude.
The altitude is now what we want for TIROS (about 450

miles) but the speed is too slow to maintain an orbit; without the additional velocity to be imparted by the third stage the satellite would fall into the atmosphere and burn up.

The third stage is mounted on a rotatable table; now the table is spun-up by several small solid rockets so that, when separated and ignited, the third stage will be spinning to maintain attitude stability and compensate for any unevenness in the burning of its propellant. The second and third stage separate, and the second stage is given a reverse thrust ("retroed") to allow the third stage and the attached TIROS to pull ahead. Separation of the second and third stages starts a timer which separates the third stage from the satellite.

The third stage is now ignited and burns for about 40 seconds. This puts both it and the satellite into a circular orbit with a velocity of nearly 17,000 miles per hour. In any satellite launching, the final propulsive stage as well as the satellite must go into orbit. Separation of the third stage and spacecraft is delayed several minutes to insure that third stage burning and "outgasing" are completed; otherwise, the third stage might bump into the satellite if given a further thrust after separation. Separation is by a spring, which pushes the satellite ahead of the third stage.

Now a second timer, activated by separation from the third stage, releases first the "TEAM" dampers and then the "Yo-Yo" despin weights. The satellite is now spinning properly in orbit, its beacons transmitting, ready to start picture taking when it first passes over a command and data acquisition station. This passage, about two hours after launch, is usually the first real proof that an orbit has been achieved.

Only in two cases have serious malfunctions occurred during the launch sequences. The TIROS II wide angle camera, starting with its first transmission and lasting throughout the useful life of the satellite, provided only pictures with much less detail than those from TIROS I. It is generally believed that the lens became fogged from the exhaust of the third stage rocket motor. Specific analyses have rejected other possibilities that were suggested: change in the position of the lens with consequent defocusing, breakage of one element of the complex lens, and movement of the vidicon surface in the camera tube. The second stage of this Delta carried no "retro" system; rather the third stage was ignited while its nozzle was still within the forward end of the second stage. The third stage thrust then provided the separation. This procedure had the supposed advantage of one less device that might malfunction; as a consequence, some of the third stage exhaust gases were apparently deflected forward and deposited on the lens surface. Fortunately, the less exposed narrow angle camera lens, and the radiation sensors, were not similarly coated.

To prevent reoccurrences, TIROS III and its successors have carried deflection shields mounted just below the satellite on the third stage rocket "bottle." Furthermore, the second stage retro system has been reinstalled on the Delta.

During the TIROS V launch, a major electron tube in the ground portion of the BTL radio guidance system failed, only a few seconds after lift-off, preventing further ground commanded guidance. The back-up inertial (gyro-controlled) system in the launch vehicle took over and kept the rocket on course, permitting a successful orbiting of the new satellite. With the back-up system, thrust continues to fuel depletion and the satellite is injected with a high velocity. This is the reason TIROS V has a significant eccentricity with the apogee (maximum orbit altitude) considerably higher than the perigee (lowest orbit altitude). But this was far better than no orbit at all; while it has slightly complicated data reduction, a great deal of valuable data was acquired during the remarkable, over-ten-month, useful life of TIROS V.

Data Acquisition Stations and Procedures

With TIROS in orbit, there now come the tasks of tracking, operating, and commanding it; and acquiring the several types of data discussed earlier.

Tracking is accomplished by the NASA Minitrack network, which uses the beacon signals. The data from the several Minitrack stations are fed into the NASA Space Computing Facility at the Goddard Space Flight Center (GSFC), just northeast of Washington, D. C. High speed computing machines use the data to predict, at frequent intervals, the location and attitude of the satellite for several days to weeks in advance.

These orbit predictions are relayed to the National Weather Satellite Center of the U. S. Weather Bureau, which uses them, recent TIROS data, other sources of weather data, and both regular and special needs (such as spacecraft launches and military operations) for weather analyses and forecasts to recommend which of the areas where cloud pictures could be taken will provide the most useful weather data. These recommendations are relayed to the TIROS Technical Control Center (TTCC), also located at GSFC.

TTCC is the combined heart and brain of day-to-day TIROS operations and decisions. In addition to the Weather Bureau recommendations, and the orbit and attitude predictions, TTCC keeps continually aware of the status of the satellite as derived from the meteorological data, and particularly from the engineering telemetry data. Based on these inputs, TTCC determines the optimum programs for operation of the satellite and relays instructions to accomplish them to the Command and Data Acquisition stations. Usually the USWB recommendations are followed, but occasionally the condition of the satellite or experimental operations desired by the NASA engineers, to aid the design of better future spacecraft, have to take precedence.

During the TIROS project, six CDA stations have been used. One of these, at the RCA plant at Hightstown, New Jersey, where TIROS was designed and built, is primarily for emergency back-up testing, and (due to the immediate availability of the engineers who designed TIROS and know it best) diagnosis of malfunctions and determination of remedies; it has been used with all the TIROS. The others have been used as tabulated below:

CDA Station Location	TIROS
Belmar, N.J. (Signal Corps Laboratory)	I, II
Kaena Point, Hawaii (USAF Facility)	I
Point Mugu, Calif. (USN Facility)	II, III, IV, V, VI, VII, VIII
Wallops Island, Virginia (NASA)	III, IV, V, VI, VII, VIII, IX, X
Fairbanks, Alaska (NASA)	VI, VII, VIII, IX, X

Basically, a CDA station consists of:

1. A large antenna to receive the comparatively weak signals from the satellite;

2. Tracking devices to keep the antenna pointed toward the satellite;

3. A radio transmitter to send commands;

4. Radio receivers to amplify and decode the signals and data received;

5. A complex console to generate command data, and to process, record, and display the data received;

6. A processing team to reduce, analyze, and transmit the weather data acquired (as will be discussed in Chapter 7);

7. Communication facilities and terminals to receive instructions from and transmit engineering data to TTCC, and to transmit the analyzed meteorological data to the USWB.

Two basic types of antennas are used. One is a 60-foot-diameter parabolic dish, officially known as the TLM-18 and illustrated in Figure 5-15. This type has been used at Belmar, Kaena Point, and Point Mugu. (A somewhat similar 85-foot

Fig. 5-15. A TLM-18 60-foot satellite tracking and data acquisition antenna. (NASA)

Fig. 5-16. TIROS data acquisition and command console. (NASA)

antenna is used at Fairbanks; it will be discussed in connection with Nimbus.) The second, known as the General Bronze after the company that builds it, consists of tuned arrays of disks mounted on a plane reflector; it is used at RCA and Wallops Island.

The console which controls all operations during a TIROS pass is shown in Figure 5-16.

To understand how these equipments are used it is best to follow what happens on a typical command and data acquisition pass. Well ahead of the time the satellite is due, all equipments are checked, and any necessary adjustments are made. Every receiver and recorder is tuned to the maximum degree feasible. Based on instructions teletyped from TTCC, the commands to be sent and the times they are to be transmitted are set into the appropriate panels of the console. Fresh recording charts, and clean magnetic tapes are placed in the various recorders. The antenna has been pointed to the position where the satellite will appear to the radio receivers as it rises above the horizon.

As the satellite comes over the horizon, beacon signals are first received. The antenna is initially moved by hand-controlled knobs to keep the signal at maximum strength. As the satellite gets about 5° above the horizon, the signal remains strong and constant; at this time, the antenna is switched to auto-track where the received signals drive a computer to keep the antenna always pointing at the TIROS. Meanwhile, the horizon scanner data, included in the beacon signals, are being recorded for later analysis to provide attitude data.

After good beacon signals are being steadily received, a command is sent to temporarily halt the horizon scanner data and to begin transmission of the engineering telemetry data. Quick inspection of these recorded data would reveal anything seriously out of line. The data will later be thoroughly analyzed to obtain the precise status of each satellite system and transmit them to TTCC.

As soon as good steady beacon signals confirm the satellite is within range for good radio reception, a so-called Alarm I (or AI) command signal is sent, which turns on and warms up the TV transmitters in the spacecraft. AI must be transmitted continuously or the satellite transmitters turn off. This is a fail-safe precaution to avoid a transmitter staying on and draining power when it is not needed, particularly after the satellite passes out of range of the CDA station. After allowing time for warm-up, the satellite may be commanded to take a few direct pictures (at 10 or 30 second intervals) of the clouds below; this is done if the time within range permits, and only if it is light enough for pictures to be taken.

Remote pictures are usually transmitted while the satellite is closest to the station. When this period starts, AII (Alarm II) is commanded to read-out first one and, after it is completed, the second of the two TV tape recorders. As each one is being read-out, concurrently the pulses which "set" the clocks in the satellite are being transmitted by the CDA to the TIROS. If the satellite contains radiation sensors, the data on the radiation tape recorder are transmitted concurrently with the read-out of one of the two TV tape recorders; this is actuated by the same signal that commands the TV recorder.

Shortly after completion of the tape recorder read-outs and the transmission of the clock setting pulses, AIII is sent at a very precise instant to start the clocks. This must be done at an exact moment or the next series of remote pictures will not be started at the proper time and so not over the desired area. Following this, any other desired commands, such as changing the setting of the magnetic attitude control coil or firing a pair of spin-up rockets, are sent.

If time remains before passing out of range, and there is sufficient power available in the storage batteries, the satellite may again be commanded to take direct TV pictures. Then usually no more than 10 minutes and at times less, after coming over the horizon, the satellite is out of range and the pass completed. The great number of things to be done in this short time makes the need for a well-designed and highly automated system self-evident. A failure could mean at best a delay in acquiring vital weather data, most likely a complete loss of some data, and at worst could result in damage to the satellite. Everything possible has been done in the design of the satellite and the station equipment to minimize this last possibility.

Even after the satellite is out of range, there is still much work to be done. The TV pictures must be developed, and a positive transparency and prints prepared, with a minimum of delay, so that the operational meteorological analysis (to be described in Chapter 7) can begin immediately. Other film magazines must be placed on the camera, and several film copies of the pictures made from the magnetic tape recording, to meet various requirements for engineering, archival and research use of the data. These copies, and the tape recordings of both the TV and radiation data, are labeled and prepared for shipment. The attitude data from the horizon scanners and radiation sensors must be transmitted to GSFC. The engineering telemetry data are extracted from the strip chart record; occurrences are extracted from an Events Recorder; and a summary report of all these data and other significant aspects of the pass are teletyped to GSFC. Any defects in the station equipment noted during the pass must be repaired. And, about 80 per cent of the time, another satellite read-out will begin only an hour and a half later. Some people may consider space projects to be glamorous; to many operators at TIROS CDA stations, the work has become as routine as most repetitive normal jobs.

Date Launched	I Apr. 1 1960	II Nov. 23 1960	III Jul. 12 1961	IV Feb. 8 1962	V June 19 1962	VI Sept. 18 1962	VII June 19 1963	VIII Dec. 21 1963
Pre-launch Designation	A-1	A-2	A-3	A-9	A-50	A-51	A-52	A-53
Approx. Weight (lbs.)	263	278	285	287	286	281	306	265
Useful TV Life (Days)	77	76 (few up to 301)	145 (231)	120 (266)	320	388	561*	376*
Useful Radiation Sensor Life (Days)	–	141 (some at 525)	81 (208)	146 (169)	–	–	561*	–
TV Sensors								
Wide-Angle	x	x	x(2)	x	x	x	x(2)	x
Narrow-Angle	x	x	–	–	–	–	–	–
Medium-Angle	–	–	–	x	x	x	–	–
APT (see Chapter 10)	–	–	–	–	–	–	–	x
Radiation Sensors								
Scanning	–	x	x	x	–	–	x	–
Medium-Angle	–	x	x	x	–	–	–	–
Omni-Directional	–	–	x	x	–	–	x	–
Magnetic Control Coil	–	x	x	x	x	x	x	x
Orbit Parameters								
Total TV pictures	22,952	36,156	35,033	32,593	58,226	66,674	95,840*	60,720*
Usable TV Pictures	19,389	22,500	24,000	23,370	48,562	59,830	87,212*	56,321*
Inclination	48.39	48.53	47.90	48.30	58.1	58.32	58.23	58.50
Apogee Alt. (St. Miles)	461.3	451.5	509.8	524.8	604	442	404	468
Perigee Alt. (St. Miles)	436.0	387.8	457.1	441.2	367	425	387	436
Period (Minutes)	99.24	98.26	100.42	100.40	100.5	98.73	97.42	99.35
Eccentricity	0.0029	0.0073	0.0059	0.0094	0.027	0.002	0.0020	0.0038

*Through December 1964. TIROS IX, a "Cartwheel", was launched Jan. 22, 1965 (p. 203); TIROS X, a conventional TIROS put in polar orbit, July 2, 1965.

6

Infrared and Other Radiation Measurements

The cloud pictures from meteorological satellites are not too difficult to understand; they significantly extend the altitudes of observation previously provided by mountain tops or airplanes. The reflection of light, which makes clouds and other objects visible to the eye or the camera, is also a common phenomenon. It is familiar because the reflection of light from the sun or an artificial source, such as a table lamp, permits us to see most objects. The almost sole exceptions are self-luminous sources, of which the sun and lamps are examples.

The other, or radiometric, observations meteorological satellites make are more difficult to understand, principally because they cannot be so directly related to our everyday experience. But they are an extension of the observations made using light.

Light is one type of electromagnetic radiation. Electromagnetic radiation consists of interrelated electrical and magnetic waves which travel together through space. There are two vital aspects of such electromagnetic waves:

1. Since they travel, and transmit energy through empty space, they provide the only way a satellite can sense what is happening on the earth and in the atmosphere below. A satellite differs from other methods of meteorological observations; other methods usually make ambient, direct contact, observations. The satellite is restricted to some form of radiation, including light, for sensing or measurement.

2. The features a satellite can sense through electromagnetic radiations vary widely with the wavelength and the frequency of vibration of the radiation. Since the wavelength, in cen-

meters, times the frequency, in cycles per seconds, of such wave always equals the velocity of light (3 × 10¹⁰ cen- meters per second, or 186,000 miles per second), specifying the wavelength determines the frequency and vice versa.

he Electromagnetic Spectrum

Light is one type of electromagnetic radiation; we are most amiliar with it because of our eyes. The reason they sense his part of the electromagnetic *spectrum* (the overall con- nuous spread of electromagnetic radiation, just as a rainbow the spectrum of just the light part) is not mysterious; it is n evolutionary adaptation to make maximum use of the egion where solar radiation reaching the surface of the earth strongest. Visible light is within the range of wavelengths om about 0.3 × 10⁻⁴ cm (0.0003 cm) (violet) to 0.8 × 10⁻⁴ m (0.0008 cm) (red), or about 10 × 10¹⁴ to 3.7 × 10¹⁴ ycles per second. The following table presents some of the ther types of radiation and their wavelengths, frequencies, c. (see page 94).

As this table shows, parts of the electromagnetic spectrum ten overlap. This is because they are just subsections of a ngle entity and, for example, what a spectroscopist may onsider as very long wavelength infrared radiation, an elec- onics engineer may consider an extremely short radio wave. he boundaries of the different regions are rather subjective ıd arbitrary. In other books, you may find slightly different oundaries given for the various regions.

Why are these different regions of radiation of interest to e meteorologist? Let us consider each of them briefly, before e pass to those of major interest; of course, some are of eater interest than others.

Gamma rays and X-rays presently interest those primarily ıcerned with the very high atmosphere and the effects on of solar radiation. These rays and their influence on the ghest atmospheric layers (they are completely absorbed fore penetrating to altitudes of several hundred thousand et) may later prove to be links between the sun and weather

Type of Electro-magnetic Radiation	Example or Further Explanation	Wavelength, Centimeters	Wavelength, Other Frequent Units	Frequency, Cycles Per Second	Frequency, Other Frequent Units
Gamma Rays	From atomic or nuclear reactions	10^{-8} and shorter	—	10^{18} and greater	—
X-Rays	Includes medical and dental	10^{-5}-10^{-9}	—	5×10^{15}-10^{19}	—
Ultraviolet Light	Waves just shorter than visible	0.3×10^{-4}-10^{-6}	3000-100 Å (Angstroms)	10^{15}-2×10^{16}	—
	Shortest ultraviolet wavelength reaching earth surface	0.29×10^{-4}	2900 Å	—	—
Visible Light		0.3×10^{-4}-0.8×10^{-4}	3000-8000 Å	3.7×10^{14}-10×10^{14}	—
	Violet Light	0.3×10^{-4}	3000 Å	10×10^{14}	—
	Red Light	0.8×10^{-4}	8000 Å	3.7×10^{14}	—
Principal Solar Radiation	Ultraviolet, visible, and infrared	10^{-3}-10^{-5}	1000 Å-10μ (microns)	10^{13}-10^{15}	—
Infrared (Thermal or Heat Radiation)	Waves just longer than visible	10^{-2}-0.8×10^{-4}	1-100μ (microns)	10^{12}-3.7×10^{14}	100-1000 cm^{-1}
	Maximum radiation near room temperature	8×10^{-4}	8μ	0.3×10^{14}	—
Microwaves	Very short radio waves	10^{2}-10^{-2}	—	10^{8} — 10^{12}	0.1-10^{3} GCS (Gigacycles)
Ultra-High Frequency (UHF)	TV Channels 14-83	10-100	—	3×10^{8}-3×10^{9}	300-3000 Mcs (Megacycles) 0.3-3 Gcs
Very-High Frequency (VHF)	TV Channels 2-13, FM Radio	100-1000	1-10 meters	3×10^{7}-3×10^{8}	30-300 Mcs
Short Wave Radio		10^{3}-10^{4}	10-100 meters	3×10^{6}-3×10^{7}	3-30 Mcs
Long Wave Radio	Commercial AM Broadcast	2×10^{4}-0.6×10^{5}	200-600 meters	5×10^{5}-1.5×10^{6}	500-1500 Kc (Kilocycles)

anges on earth. Here, however, we will pass them by without further discussion.

Ultraviolet constitutes a significant part of the sun's radiaon, although only a small portion can penetrate to the ound. Ultraviolet may be vital to measuring the true extent variations in the sun's energy output. Measurements in the nger wavelength ultraviolet are used to determine the nount of ozone in the upper atmosphere; ozone (a threeom molecule of oxygen) is concentrated principally near ,000 feet above the earth's surface. Measurements of its nount are used to trace both horizontal and vertical air otions at these levels. Measurements from a satellite in her parts of the ultraviolet have been suggested as a way to termine cloud top altitudes.

Visible light is the part of the spectrum used to obtain the IROS cloud pictures. Visible light comes from objects, such the sun, which are hot enough to be self-luminous (generatg radiation), with sufficient energy at wave lengths our eyes n detect. Solar radiation over its whole range (ultraviolet, sible where it is most intense, and infrared) is the source essentially all the earth's energy and of the basic energy iving the atmosphere.

The infrared is the region where objects and gases of rmal temperatures (say $-100°F$ to $+100°F$) radiate most ongly. (Such objects could be said to be "self-luminous," t the energy is concentrated in frequencies where our eyes e not sensitive.) The infrared is the region where the earth d its atmosphere radiate energy back to space. (On the erage this must equal the net incoming solar radiation, or e earth would continuously warm up or cool down.) Infrad radiations can be used to measure the temperatures of the rth's surface and of atmospheric layers, and the amounts of rious gases.

Microwaves are used much as infrared radiations to measure nospheric temperatures and compositions. Such measurents will be discussed in Chapter 14.

UHF, VHF, and similar radio waves of frequencies greater an 10 Mcs are used to communicate between the earth and

satellites. (At frequencies below about 10 Mcs, most of th
signal is absorbed by the ionosphere.) Radio wavelengths i
these regions are used to command TIROS and to transm
its data to the ground. Possible ways of making meteorologic:
observations using these radio wavelengths include: (1) sferic
the radio signal or static from lightning, and (2) rada
reflected very short radio waves used to detect precipitatio
These will be discussed in Chapter 14.

In this chapter, we will deal principally with the ultraviole
visible, and infrared part of the spectrum. These radiations a
produced by the heat inherent in all objects and gases (sinc
none are at absolute zero). The hotter an object or gas, th
greater the amount of radiation it emits and the higher the fr
quency (shorter the wavelength) where the greatest amou
of radiation is emitted. For gases, the greater the amount
the gas, the greater the energy radiated.

The sun has a surface temperature of about 6000°, abs
lute or Kelvin (K). Radiation from it is most intense at a fe
tenths of a micron wavelength. Although small amounts
solar radiation exist at all wavelengths, at the top of the atmo
phere significant amounts are concentrated between 1000
at the short wavelength end and a few microns at the lor
wavelength end. At the edge of the atmosphere, the tot
intensity of solar radiation is about two calories per squa:
centimeter per minute.

In contrast, the earth's surface has a temperature of abo
0°-20°C. Its wave length of peak radiation is about 10 micron
and most of the energy is concentrated between about tw
and 40 microns wave length. Below about 4 microns, th
intensity of infrared emitted from the earth is less than th
of solar radiation reaching the earth; above the four micr
region, the infrared radiation is the stronger. Average infrare
intensities of the earth and atmosphere are a few tenths of
calorie per square centimeter per minute. If you like pro
lems, you may care to show that the average intensity of th
infrared radiation emitted by the earth and its atmosphe
must be 25 per cent of the intensity of the absorbed sol
radiation.

The sun, the earth's surface, and clouds emit radiation over . continuous band of wavelengths with the energy at various wavelengths varying with temperature. Gases are different; hey emit and absorb radiations most intensely in preferred wavelengths and bands of wavelengths which vary with the ;as.

For a given wavelength, all substances which are good absorbers are also efficient emitters and vice versa. Absorption, however, is a function principally of the amount of energy alling on the body, essentially regardless of its temperature, while the intensity of the radiation emitted is principally a unction of temperature. The efficiency of absorption and emission of a substance usually varies with wave length. For example, fresh snow is a poor absorber (good reflector) of visible light (0.4 micron wave lengths) while it is an excellent emitter (and absorber) of infrared (10 micron wave length). Thus, a snow cover stays by reflecting sunlight in the daytime while it loses heat in the infrared at all times. A dull black stove, on the other hand, is obviously a good absorber of visible light and also a good absorber and emitter, of infrared ays, and therefore efficient for heating.

To discuss fully the radiations of the various gases in the atmosphere would require a book. We can be satisfied with he following general tabulation:

Gas	Regions of strong absorption and emission
Water Vapor	4-8 microns, most strongly about 6 microns
Carbon Dioxide	Above 12 microns, most strongly about 15 microns
Ozone	Below about 3000 Å; narrow band about 9.6 microns

Meteorological Satellite Radiation Observations

With the above cursory discussion of radiation as a background, what can we measure from a meteorological satellite using radiation detectors?

Since the sun is the only significant source of energy to maintain the earth's average temperature, and to drive the atmosphere, we would like to measure precisely the intensity of this radiation and its variations. From measurements on high mountain tops in arid regions, where absorption is a minimum, plus theoretically calculated corrections, we know that the average energy of sun's rays just outside the atmosphere is very nearly two calories per square centimeter per minute. Because any variation in this quantity is of the order of the current accuracy of measurement, it has come to be known as the *solar constant*. Because we must estimate corrections for the ultraviolet portion of the radiation, where it is likely that variations are most intense, and for absorption of water vapor bands, our measurements of the solar constant may be in error by about one per cent. Thus any small variations could not be detected.

Obviously, any radiometer designed for useful measurements of the solar constant from a satellite, above the absorbing atmosphere, must be extremely precise as regards both the absolute intensity of solar radiation and any variations. Hanel (see Reference 6-1) has designed such an experiment, which is expected to be flown on one of the Orbiting Solar Observatory (OSO) satellites.

All the solar radiation entering the earth's atmosphere is not absorbed. About a third is reflected back to space by clouds, by the earth's surface, and by the atmosphere itself. This reflected radiation, in the same wavelengths as the incoming solar radiation, is not available to drive the atmospheric heat engine. The percentage of incoming solar radiation reflected is known as the *albedo*. TIROS and Explorer VII have carried sensors which permit measuring the albedo. Of interest is not only the overall average albedo, but also its variation with time and space so that its local converse, the absorption of solar radiation, can be known.

The average total outgoing radiation emitted by the earth and its atmosphere (in infrared wavelengths, because of their temperatures) must equal the average absorbed solar radiation. However, the outgoing infrared radiation varies considerably with time and area. As discussed in Chapter 3, we can consider the incoming solar radiation as the fuel that drives the atmospheric engine and the emitted infrared radiaion as its exhaust. By measuring and studying the variations f this "exhaust," we can learn more about the atmospheric ngine. These measurements have also been made by both 'IROS and Explorer VII, as will be described later.

The temperatures of the ground surface of the earth, of the urfaces of the oceans, and of various levels in the atmosphere re commonly measured by conventional instruments such as hermometers and radiosondes. To a greater or lesser degree, hese measurements can also be made from satellites. Consider rst the temperatures of the earth's land and sea surfaces. Assume we are over a cloud-free area. In an interval of the pectrum where the atmosphere is completely transparent neither absorbs nor emits radiation), any radiant energy neasured would come from the earth's surface. The amount f energy emitted is a function of the temperature. Accordngly, if we know the spectral interval within which the neasurements are made, the response of the sensor, and any leparture of the surface from a perfect emitter, we can calulate the surface temperature. Completely transparent regions f the spectrum are almost non-existent, but there are some hat come close enough to permit useful measurements. Such neasurements have been made by TIROS, and by the greatly mproved instrumentation on Nimbus.

If an overcast covers the area at which the temperature-neasuring sensor is directed, the temperature measured will e that of the cloud top. Since the temperature of the atmos-here usually decreases with height, cloud tops are usually older than the surface of the earth. Therefore, if a sensor canning the earth notes a significant decrease in temperature, t has very likely crossed from a cloud-free to a cloud-covered rea. This provides a method of detecting cloud-covered areas t night, when the TV cameras cannot operate.

The rate of decrease with height of atmospheric tempera-ure is more or less uniform, so the cloud top temperature ;ives a rough measure of the cloud top height. If accurate neasurements of atmospheric temperatures at various heights re made concurrently, the cloud top height can be deduced ccurately.

Measurements from a satellite of the temperatures at various levels in the atmosphere are more difficult. Methods of doing it have, however, been suggested by such scientists as Kaplan (see Reference 6-2) and King (see Reference 6-3); and equipments for making these measurements are being developed.

These measurements use a gas which is a good emitter of particular wavelengths of radiation and so is also a good absorber at these same wavelengths. Consider a gas of constant distribution through the lower atmosphere, such as carbon dioxide, and a spectral region where it is the only absorbing atmospheric gas and where its absorption changes steadily as a function of wavelength, as shown in the top part of Figure 6-1. In wavelength region A, where absorption is the greatest, all radiation leaving the atmosphere and reaching the satellite sensors comes from near the top of the atmosphere. Radiation in these wavelengths originating lower 'n the atmosphere, or from the ground, is absorbed in the atmosphere and does not reach the satellite sensors. (This energy may later be re-emitted as radiation, but then it originates, for our purposes, in the layer where it was absorbed.)

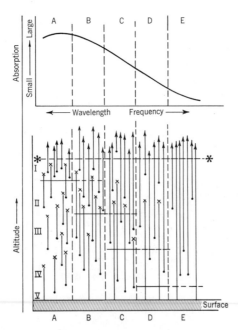

Fig. 6-1. Use of change of absorption with wavelength to measure atmospheric temperatures.

Accordingly, the radiation measured by the satellite at these wavelengths corresponds to an average temperature near the top of the atmosphere. The average is taken with regard to density, so the measurement is most strongly influenced by the lower portions of this upper part of the atmosphere. These events are shown in Figure 6-1, at the left portion of the bottom part. The dash-line with a star at each end represents the "top" of the atmosphere. In wavelength region A, all the radiation leaving the atmosphere originates near the top, in layer I. Radiation from the lower layers (II, III, IV, and V), and from the surface, is absorbed within the atmosphere. Thus, the energy reaching the satellite is representative of the temperature in layer I.

Similarly, using the less absorptive wavelength region B, an average of the temperature for layers I and II combined is obtained. Since the temperature of layer I is now known from the region A measurement, the temperature for layer II can be calculated; in this, the greater influence of layer II, due to its greater density, is a help.

In analogous fashion, wavelength band C measures the average temperature of layers I, II, and III; wavelength band D that of layers I, II, III, and IV. From the earlier measurements, the temperatures of all but the lowest of the measured layers are known and that of the lowest can then be calculated. Eventually there is a wavelength band (shown by E in Figure 6-1) where some of the radiation leaving the atmosphere comes from the surface or from cloud tops. This puts a lower limit on the altitude for which the temperature can be deduced. This limit, somewhat above the actual level of the surface or the cloud top, is shown in Figure 6-1 as the top of layer V.

In practice, the measurement of temperature by this method is more complicated than described above and illustrated in Figure 6-1. Complications arise because we are dealing with a continuum of altitudes and wavelengths, rather than the discrete segments shown in Figure 6-1. Nevertheless, the basic principles are those described above. The number of layers into which the atmosphere can be practically divided for measurement depends on the narrowness of the spectra interval possible in the sensors. Kaplan (see Reference 6-2) has suggested using ten layers. The instrumentation presently being developed is expected to measure four layers at level above 500 mb (18,000 feet); it will be discussed in Chapter 14

King's approach (see Reference 6-3) is different in that i uses a single, partially absorbed wavelength, but looks at the atmosphere at several different angles. The greater the angle between the vertical and the direction of view, the highe the layer from which the emitted radiation originates. (Whe looking at an angle, more atmosphere is penetrated to reacl a given altitude.) Accordingly, the temperature near the to of the atmosphere comes from an angle well away from the vertical; at lesser angles, the temperatures of progressively deeper layers are measured. Since temperature normally de creases with increasing altitude, the amount of radiation received decreases with increased angle from the vertical or as the horizon or edge of the earth is approached. The edge of a planet is known as the *limb,* and so King's approacl is known as the *limb-darkening* technique. Similar approaches were used by Mariner II in measuring the temperatures o Venus and its atmosphere.

King's technique requires only a single sensor since the measurement is made at a single wavelength. It has the dis advantages that the sensor must scan through a range of angles and particularly that the areas where the temperatures of the several layers are measured are not directly above each other

The final measurement to be discussed, before proceeding to those actually made by TIROS, is atmospheric composition i.e., how much of a variable gas there is in a column of the atmosphere, and how it is distributed with altitude. The vari able gases of most interest in the atmosphere are water vapo and ozone. Water vapor is of obvious interest since it is related to the presence or absence of clouds and precipitation Ozone, concentrated near 80,000 feet, is useful in tracing ai motions at high levels.

To measure the total amount of gas in a column of air, two wavelengths close together are selected, preferably in the

visible, ultraviolet, or shorter wavelength infrared where reflected sunshine can be used. One wavelength must not be
absorbed by the gas to be measured; in the other, the gas
should absorb partially but not completely, leaving enough
radiation to be measured by the satellite. Because the wavelengths are close together, it is assumed that the reflected
sunlight, and any absorption by other gases, are the same
at both wavelengths. Accordingly, the difference in the amount
of energy measured can be attributed to absorption by the gas
and used to calculate its total amount. Similar techniques can
be used with infrared radiation emitted from the surface, but
they require a knowledge of the temperature structure of the
atmosphere and assumptions as to the altitude distribution
of the gas being measured.

The distribution with height of a gas can be measured using
the procedure described for measuring the vertical distribution of temperature (Figure 6-1). First, however, the temperature distribution must be known (presumably from this technique applied to a gas whose amount and distribution is
constant). The measurement at each different wavelength is
a function of both the amount and temperature of the gas
but, since the temperature is already known, the amount of
variable gas can be calculated. This technique is most likely
to be applied to water vapor, using the 6.3 micron band.

The TIROS Radiation Sensors

TIROS II, III, IV, and VII have made radiation measurements. (TIROS V was also so equipped, but the subsystem was
disconnected prior to launch because of a malfunction. Launch
was not delayed to permit repairs, to insure picture coverage
of 1962 hurricanes.) Three types of sensors have been used:
(1) a five channel scanning radiometer, (2) a two channel
medium-angle radiometer, and (3) a two channel omni-
directional radiometer.

The five channel radiometer is the more important of the
three. It makes the following measurements, as shown in
Figure 6-2:

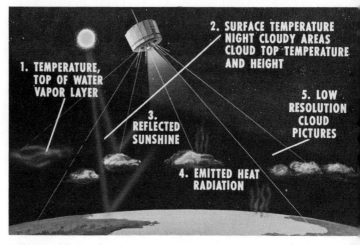

Fig. 6-2.   TIROS infrared measurements. (NASA)

Channel 1   6.3 microns (actually about 5.9-6.7 microns) This is a region of maximum water vapor absorption and accordingly, this sensor measures the temperature near the top of atmospheric water vapor. On the average, this is a temperature near 25,000 feet. However, the amount and distribution of water vapor vary considerably, and the level of measurement may be much lower, as over a desert or higher as in the moist tropics. Low values, or cold temperatures, indicate large amounts of water vapor extending to great altitudes; high values and higher temperatures indicate less water vapor concentrated nearer the surface.

Channel 2   8-12 micron atmospheric *window* (region of low absorption). This sensor measures surface or cloud top temperatures, and detects areas of cloud cover at night.

Channel 3   0.2-5 microns albedo. This measures reflected solar radiation.

Channel 4   7-30+ microns. This measures the total outgoing long wave radiation from the earth and the atmosphere, the "exhaust" of the atmospheric "engine."

Channel 5   0.5-0.7 microns. This measures reflected solar radiation at the wavelengths to which the TV cameras are sensitive. It detects cloud cover in daytime for use in analyzing the data from the other sensors, especially when the TV cameras are not operating.

In TIROS VII, the normal Channel 1 sensor was replaced by a 14-16 micron carbon dioxide sensor. It measures the appearance of the earth's horizon at these wavelengths and aided in the development of the Nimbus horizon sensors, which control the Nimbus stabilization system (see Reference 6-4). These measurements and those from the 6.3 micron sensors can also be considered initial experiments toward the development of techniques for measuring the vertical distribution of temperature and water vapor.

The sensors are mounted in the satellite so that each one (the five operate concurrently in parallel) rapidly looks alternately in opposite directions, at an angle of 45° to the spin axis of the satellite (see Figure 6-3). At least one of the opposite directions is always pointed toward space, which serves as a reference at a temperature near +4°K. One direction of scan is produced by the rotation of the satellite about its spin axis; the other by the motion of the satellite in its orbit around the earth. Because of the various orientations of the spin axis relative to the earth, several different scan patterns are possible, as shown in Figure 6-4, and usually all occur during different parts of an orbit. When the spin axis is nearly straight down, only one direction of view intersects the earth, tracing an interconnected and overlapping, approximately circular figure much like a common penmanship exercise. When the spin axis is nearly parallel to the surface of the earth, both directions alternately scan the earth in U-shaped patterns—one ahead and one behind the satellite subpoint. In intermediate positions, one or both sensors may scan, depending on the attitude.

The operation of one of the five parallel channels is shown in Figure 6-3. The radiation is reflected, by a mirror prism, onto a rotating chopper wheel. Assume one direction is scanning the earth; the other, of course, is pointing toward space and acting as the reference. The chopper is half-reflective (a mirror) and half non-reflective (black); as it rotates first the

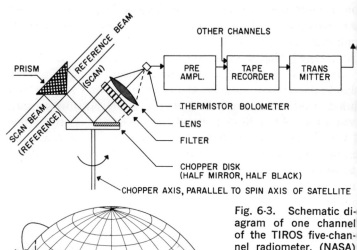

Fig. 6-3. Schematic diagram of one channel of the TIROS five-channel radiometer. (NASA)

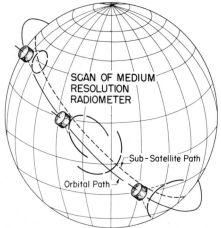

Fig. 6-4. Geometry of the scanning motions of the TIROS five-channel radiometer. (NASA)

radiation from one direction (in this case the earth) and then from the other (space) is reflected onto the filter, lens, and sensing thermister. The chopper rotates at 2400 rpm (as against the satellite spin of about 10 rpm) so during any very short portion of the earth scan both the earth and the reference energy are alternately focused on the sensor. The instrument measures the difference in these energies. The energy reflected from the mirror part of the chopper passes through a filter, which excludes wavelengths not to be measured by that channel, and a lens which focuses the energy on a thermistor bolometer. The bolometer acts like a very sensitive and rapidly responding thermometer; it converts the radiation energy to an electrical voltage proportional to the energy falling on the bolometer.

Because of the rapid alternation of space and earth views, due to the chopper rotation, the voltage leaving the bolometer has a wave-shape alternation, and so produces an A.C. current with a 40 cycle per second frequency and an amplitude (wave height) proportional to the difference in the space and earth signal. The amplitude thus measures the energy of the radiation from the earth or its atmosphere. It is amplified and fed to the recorder, and later, on command, to the transmitter.

A trace of the recorded amplitude, after processing on the ground, is shown in Figure 6-5. This is a recording of some Channel 2 (atmospheric window) data during a period when both directions of view were alternately scanning the earth. During intervening short periods, both were looking simultaneously at space. The simultaneous views of space are the four sections near the bottom, two of which are intersected by the heavy vertical bars. Three periods of earth or atmosphere scan are shown, approximately equally spaced, between

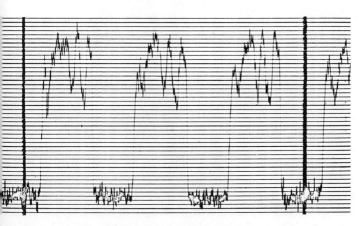

Fig. 6-5.   Trace on a strip recording chart of the data from the 8-12 micron channel of the TIROS scanning radiometer. (NASA)

the vertical bars. During these periods, the trace is fluctuating about midway on the chart. Look more closely at the middle sweep (above the heavy triangle at the bottom) starting at its left end. After the simultaneous space scan which provides a calibrating reference, the trace climbs almost vertically. This is the rapid increase in temperature at the horizon. The trace then oscillates for a while lower than its later values; this probably represents the colder temperatures of cloud cover. Then it climbs, probably a clear, warm area. Before the final rapid drop as it sweeps off the other horizon, note two more apparent cloud-covered (cooler) and two more apparent clear (warmer) regions.

The electronics that accept the radiation signals from the

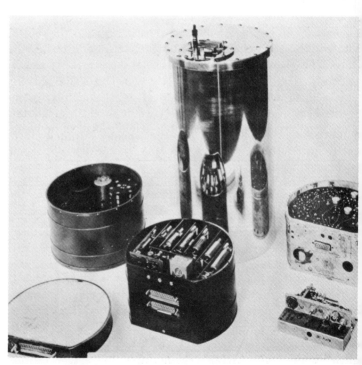

Fig. 6-6. The electronics and tape recorder of the TIROS scanning radiometer. (NASA)

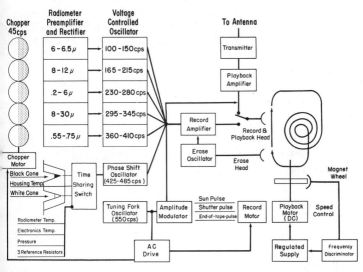

Fig. 6-7. Schematic block diagram of the TIROS radiometer electronics. (NASA)

five parallel channels, and from the other TIROS radiometers, and the recorder that stores them, are shown in Figure 6-6 and, schematically in Figure 6-7. Referring to Figure 6-7, the amplitude signal from each channel is confined within a different frequency band. For example, the signal from Channel 1 is confined to the range 100-150 cycles per second (cps); that from Channel 2 to 165-215 cps. This is done by adding a fixed frequency, different for each channel, to the original, 40 cps frequency produced by the chopper. For example, the Channel 1 local oscillator adds about 85 cps; the Channel 2 about 150 cps, etc. Then, the signals from all five channels, and from the other radiometers, can be added, and recorded and transmitted together. This is known as frequency multiplexing.

To a certain degree, frequency multiplexing can be thought of as similar to using different colored insulations for identifying each of a mass of wires running through a multiple-wire cable. Since different colors are equivalent to different frequencies of visible light, this increases the extent of this analogy.

To separate the signals after transmission to the ground the combined signal is run through a series of *band-pass filters*. When this is done, the filter for the Channel 1 Data passes signals between 100 and 150 cps, but only those signals. This separation on the ground is referred to as *demultiplexing*.

In the satellite, the combined signals are recorded on a continuously running endless loop tape recorder, so well built that, in TIROS II, it was still able to provide useful data more than 17 months after launch. This was in spite of the fact that its pressurized container (Figure 6-6) had several months earlier developed a leak. The leak exposed the recorder, its bearings and lubricants to the vacuum of space. The length of tape permits slightly more than one orbit's data to be recorded; if not then read-out, the earlier data are progressively erased as new data are recorded. Upon a signal from the CDA station, the recorder speeds up by a factor of 30:1, and plays back the data through the 237 Mcs transmitter. After completion of readout, the recorder automatically reverts to the record mode.

Multiplexed onto the recorder are not only the data from the five-channel and other radiometers but also data on the operation of the radiometers, and on the times when the TV pictures are taken.

A second type of TIROS radiometer is shown schematically in the lower left of Figure 6-7. This radiometer, flown in TIROS II, III, and IV, consists of two detectors each mounted in a separate cone which restricts the field of view to a few hundred miles as against the approximately thirty miles of the scanning radiometer. This field of view coincides with that of the wide-angle TV cameras, permitting the radiometer data to be compared with the amount of cloudiness observed. One detector is white and reflects most solar radiation. It responds almost solely to emitted thermal radiation longer than about 4 microns. The second is black and responds to all radiation between about 0.2 and 40 microns. It measures a combination of both reflected solar and emitted thermal radiation. Both should give the same reading at night (no reflected solar radiation) and this is one way to confirm their proper operation. During daytime, the reflected solar radiation is determined by subtracting the reading of the white sensor from that of the black. This gives the albedo. The albedo, subtracted from the incoming solar radiation (as computed from the solar constant), gives the solar energy absorbed by the earth and its atmosphere. The white readings are a direct measure of the long wave radiation lost to space by the earth and atmosphere.

A third radiometer, flown on TIROS III, IV, and VII, was developed by Prof. V. Suomi of the University of Wisconsin. It partially duplicates the experiment he designed for Vanguard and successfully flew on Explorer VII. The Explorer data have shown a distinct correlation between areas of reduced long-wave radiation and storms (see Reference 4-10). This is due, of course, to lower radiation from the colder cloud tops than from clear areas.

The Suomi radiation detectors consist of four hemispheres, about the diameter of ping-pong balls. Two are black and two are white. Black and white pairs are mounted on opposite sides of the TIROS on extended brackets, with mirror backings which prevent them from seeing the satellite. In this configuration, the two white and two black hemispheres respond like a single white and a single black ball isolated in space at the position of the satellite. They measure radiation from all directions, including that from the sun, and are often referred to as omni-directional. The white body responds only to long wave radiation, while the black body measures energy at all wave lengths between about 0.2 and 40 microns. The sensors are thermisters inside each hemisphere.

Since radiant energy decreases with the square of the distance from the source, and the surface of the earth curves, the radiations measured by these detectors come principally from circles of perhaps 1000 miles in diameter. Even within these circles, the radiometers respond most to the central portions.

To obtain the albedo from these omnidirectional radiometers both the direct solar energy, calculated from the solar constant, and the energy measured by the white body must be subtracted from the reading of the black body. Otherwise, except for the area measured, the measurement is identical to that from the medium resolution detectors.

As shown in Figure 6-7 for the cone detectors (the omni-directional detectors are similarly treated), the medium resolution and omni-directional data are time-shared by a commutator (multi-position switch) along with other data on the radiometer performance and calibrations. These data share a sixth channel which is frequency multiplexed with the five scanning radiometer channels and fed to the endless loop tape recorder.

7

Processing and Presentation of TIROS Data

At the TIROS Data Acquisition Stations, the satellite data are made ready for use.

Cloud Picture Data

The TIROS pictures are recorded on 35-mm film by a CDA kinescope camera, either during satellite readout or by playback of the magnetic tape. This film is immediately processed to provide both 35-mm transparencies for projection and prints for overlaying of geographic reference grids.

To know where the clouds in the pictures are located, it is necessary to know where the satellite was and the direction of the camera when the picture was taken. The position of the satellite is established by its orbit and the time of the picture; from which the point on the earth under the satellite (called the sub-satellite point), and the satellite's altitude, can be computed. The camera direction is determined by the satellite attitude. Horizon scanner attitudes are often in error and the best attitudes are from the pictures themselves. Although attitude is determined from other data, a check of attitude from the pictures is made at frequent intervals.

Attitude is determined by measuring the distance between the horizon and the center (*Principle Point*) of the picture. The nearest point on the horizon is on the straight line that connects the subpoint of the satellite (the point directly under the spacecraft) and the Principal Point (see Reference 7-G-3). This line establishes one aspect of the attitude, the *azimuth* of the spin axis, or its direction relative to north.

Determining the angle between the spin axis and the vertical (the nadir angle) can be accomplished from ordinary geometry and trigonometry (see Reference 7-G-3). The nadir angle, n, is given by:

$$n = \text{arc} \sin \frac{R}{R + h} - \text{arc} \tan S/f, \qquad \text{where}$$

R, the radius of the earth, is known;

h, the altitude of the satellite, can be determined from orbit data;

f, the camera focal length, was measured before launch, and

S, the distance between the picture center and the horizon can be measured on the picture.

Accordingly, from this equation and a measurement on the picture, the nadir angle and so the other aspect of the satellite attitude can be determined.

Having established the satellite location and attitude, a picture and its features can be located. For each picture, each point on the vidicon surface and so on the picture has one and only one corresponding point on the earth. Except for lens distortions, for which adjustments can be made, a straight line could be drawn from each earth point through the lens center to its corresponding point on the vidicon surface.

In the early days of TIROS, this technique was developed. From the satellite position and attitude, the point on the earth

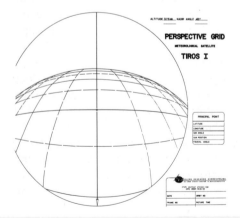

Fig. 7-1. A rectangular grid on the earth as it would appear from TIROS (also known as a Perspective Grid). (ARACON Geophysics Co., USAF)

of the center of the picture can be determined from this relationship:

$$B = \text{arc sin} \left[\left(\frac{R+h}{R} \right) \sin n \right] - n$$

where n, R, and h have previously been defined and B is the distance, in degrees of great circle arc, between the satellite subpoint and the principal point (picture center).

Imagine a rectangular grid inscribed *on the earth's surface* with its center at the picture center, one central line as a great circle running through the picture center and the sub-satellite point, and the other central line a second great circle perpendicular to the first. The remainder of the grid consists of lines, parallel to the central ones, at distances of three degrees of great circle arc or just about two hundred statute miles.

If this grid were now viewed from TIROS, it would look something like Figure 7-1 which is usually referred to as a *Perspective Grid* because it gives a perspective view of how the rectangular grid on the earth would appear. Of course, the appearance would vary with the altitude and attitude (nadir angle) of TIROS at the instant the pictures were taken.

For use with TIROS, a library of grids like that in Figure 7-1 was computed for the various altitudes and nadir angles from which TIROS was expected to take pictures (see Reference 7-G-2). Figure 7-1 is just one of such grids, specifically for a satellite altitude of 375 nautical miles and a nadir angle of 45°.

To use these grids, the TIROS picture to be located is placed in a projector (Figure 7-2) and focused on a working surface to the same scale as that used for the perspective grids. Then the proper grid, chosen for the altitude and nadir angle at which the picture was taken, is placed under the projector; the grid is slid and rotated until the principal points and horizon of both grid and picture match; this pro-vides a check on the proper grid choice. The grid projected on the picture looks like Figure 7-3a. The features in the

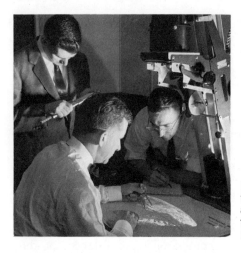

Fig. 7-2.   Use of projector and grids for locating and rectifying TIROS pictures.   (ARACON Geophysics Co.)

picture can now be related to positions on the earth relative to the grid we imagined drawn on the earth. The significant features are sketched on the perspective grid for further use (Figure 7-3b).

Each position and distorted square in a perspective grid has a one-to-one relation to that in a rectangular *transfer grid* (the rectangular grid imagined inscribed on the earth, now drawn to a scale to fit weather maps). Using this, we

Fig. 7-3a. TIROS picture projected on perspective grid. (ARACON)

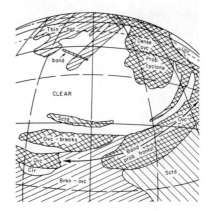

Fig. 7-3b. Significant cloud and other data sketched onto perspective grid. (ARACON)

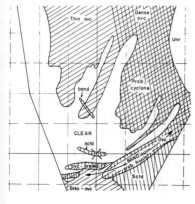

Fig. 7-3c. Transfer of significant data to Transfer Grid. (ARACON)

Fig. 7-3d. Transfer of sketched data to conventional latitude-longitude grid. (ARACON)

re-sketch the significant features in Figures 7-3a and 3b in their proper position on the transfer grid to get Figure 7-3c. This provides a sketch of how the features would look from directly above rather than from the angle at which the picture was taken; we have now *rectified* the picture, i.e., returned the various features to their proper relative scale, thus removing the effects of perspective. But we still need to locate the cloud patterns and other features.

To accomplish this last step, we place an appropriate map (the same scale as the transfer grid) over the transfer grid with the principal point located under its actual point on the map, and the picture features on the transfer grid properly oriented relative to the directions on the overlaid map. The features are then traced onto the map (Figure 7-3d), providing the cloud data in a form usable by the meteorologist.

The above process is obviously lengthy, cumbersome, and tedious. Electronic data processing equipment now permits an equivalent alternative procedure to be used at a significant saving of manpower and effort (see Reference 7-G-3). Based on data on the satellite position and attitude, a computer

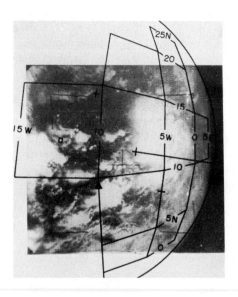

Fig. 7-4.   Latitude-longitude grid (in perspective) drawn on a TIROS picture. (ARACON Geophysics Co.)

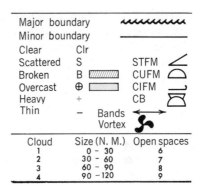

Fig. 7-5. Symbols used in TIROS nephanalyses. (USWB)

calculates and draws a latitude-longitude grid at the same perspective as the view from the satellite. This latitude-longitude grid can then be traced directly on the picture (Figure 7-4). From this, the significant features are sketched directly onto a standard map which, because of the use of a perspective latitude-longitude grid, serves as its own transfer grid.

The computer method was developed during TIROS II and made the standard system for TIROS III and later models. The hand system is retained for emergencies, such as computer failures.

These various TIROS gridding and location techniques were developed and implemented by Dr. Arnold Glaser and his associates of ARACON Geophysics Company in cooperation with the Air Force, the U. S. Weather Bureau, and NASA.

For sketching of the significant cloud features, a standardized notation was adopted (Figure 7-5). Most of the description in Figure 7-5 is self-explanatory; not necessarily evident are the cloud-type categories.

    STFM—stratiform; i.e., layer-like clouds
    CUFM—cumuliform; i.e., vertically-developing clouds
    CIFM—cirriform; i.e., high, ice-crystal clouds
    CB—cumulonimbus; i.e., heavy towering cumulus and thunderstorms.

At the TIROS data station, nephanalyses of all contiguous pictures from the same orbit are combined on a single map. As soon as it is completed and checked, it is transmitted by *facsimile* to the National Weather Satellite Center (NWSC), located in the National Meteorological Center (NMC) at Suitland, Maryland. There it is further checked against other available data to prevent dissemination of erroneous data. In order that many may benefit by the information obtained, the final nephanalysis is given at least four types of distribution:

1. Copies are given to the analysts of the NMC for incorporation with other meteorological data in the preparation of weather analyses and forecasts for the United States and other areas.

2. Copies are sent to other weather services and stations, by wire facsimile within North America, and by radio facsimile to U. S. military weather services and foreign weather services overseas. Widescale radio-facsimile broadcasts overseas were begun in mid-1962, and have been favorably received by foreign countries.

3. Coded nephanalyses, in a form suitable for teletype transmission, are prepared and disseminated. Although less detailed than the facsimile pictures, they are the best method of providing the data to foreign countries unable to receive radio facsimile.

4. Copies of the nephanalyses are filed for later use in research and climatological projects.

Two other products of the cloud picture processing are also provided by the data stations. Even before the completion of the nephanalyses, flash warnings are disseminated by telephone, cable, or other means whenever severe weather conditions are first noted or when major changes or developments are spotted. Starting in 1962, limited numbers of the gridded pictures or mosaics are sent by a special photo-facsimile to the NMC and from there to a few major Weather Bureau stations. However, the time to transmit such pictures and the special communications required present far higher requirements than for the sketch nephanalyses. These pictures can only supplement the nephanalyses by providing more detail to those relatively few weather stations and centers that can receive them.

Examples of the many uses that have been made of the TIROS cloud picture data in operational weather analysis and forecasting will be discussed in Chapter 8.

Archiving of the Cloud Pictures for Research Use

Although weather data are very perishable as applied to forecasting, they have continued value for research towards improved forecasting and a better basic understanding of the atmosphere and in climatology, the statistical study of typical weather conditions and their interrelationship and variations.

To meet these requirements, high quality negatives of all the TV data are prepared from the magnetic tapes by replaying them through the kinescope. If necessary, further re-runs are made to insure the highest quality negatives. This master negative is carefully edited. When in the best possible condition, the master negative is shipped to the National Weather Records Center (NWRC), Asheville, North Carolina, a branch of the National Archives of the United States operated by the Weather Bureau for all the U.S. weather services. This master is used only to make a reproduction master negative and positive or replacements for them, and it is then carefully preserved as an archives copy of the TIROS data. The reproduction masters, copied from it, are used as working masters from which further copies are made for research meteorologists and climatologists both in the United States and overseas.

As soon as possible after a TIROS ceases to provide useful data and editing of the master negative can be completed, a final catalog of the data is issued (see References 7-1, 7-2). The TIROS data, as listed in those catalogs, is organized into 100-foot rolls of 35-mm film (both positives and negatives), each roll containing the pictures from about a dozen orbits. They can be purchased for $6.50 per hundred-foot roll of either positive or negative film. A full roll must be purchased; requests for lesser quantities or other forms will not be honored. Requests for catalogs or film purchases should be sent to the National Weather Records Center. The purchaser can use the negatives to make his own prints or shorter lengths of 35-mm positive filmstrips.

For those few cases where the special requirements of research workers cannot be met by these NWRC films, special requests for unusual forms of the data will be considered, in terms of their merit and feasibility, by the National Weather Satellite Center.

Processing of the Radiation Data

Because of the complexity of processing these data, and the presently less obvious ways to apply them to weather analysis, no attempt has been yet made to put the radiation data to real time use except as an aid in determining satellite attitude. This discussion will be limited to processing for research use.

At the readout station, the only processing is a check of signal quality during recording on magnetic tape. The tapes, which are the primary record of these data, are then shipped to NASA's Goddard Space Flight Center.

For spot checking of the early data from each satellite, samples of the data are recorded as line tracings on strip charts. This form of the data was shown in Figure 6-5. From these recordings, by laborious hand techniques, it is possible to read off the radiation values, and to determine (using the orbit and attitude data) the locations of the points. Such processing is so laborious that it is limited to:

1. Early samples, for spot checking of the data quality.

2. Early samples, where special research requirements cannot wait for machine processing.

3. Studies toward the development or improvement of machine processing techniques.

4. Special studies, such as the high resolution and extremely precise plotting of the data by Dr. T. Fujita of the University of Chicago, which require processing beyond that possible with the standard machine techniques.

The great bulk of the radiation data, however, makes

machine processing a must if they are to be reduced economically within a reasonable time. The major steps, shown in Figure 7-6, will be explained below.

The analog (magnetic) tape is played through an analog-to-digital converter (not shown in Figure 7-6, but between the "Analog Tape" and "Digital Tape" blocks) to change the analog (continuous) form of the data (shown in Figure 6-5) to discreet digital quantities (i.e., specific numbers) that can be accepted by the computer. These digital values of the observations, and various ancillary data such as the radiometer temperature, are recorded on a second magnetic tape in a form acceptable to the computer.

A second type of needed information is satellite position and attitude. As can be seen in the upper right of Figure 7-6, the position data comes from the Minitrack station satellite tracking data. The attitude comes from an optimized combination of the various types of satellite attitude data, including measurments of photographs, horizon sensor data, magnetic attitude

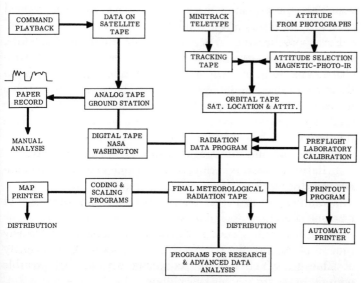

Fig. 7-6. Schematic diagram of the flow of TIROS radiation data during the course of its processing. (NASA)

control coil settings (discussed in Chapter 5), and data from the radiometer measurements themselves. The orbit and satellite attitude data are combined on another magnetic tape as a second computer input.

The third input is preflight calibrations of the radiometer, relating the measurements and ancillary readings such as radiometer temperature to the radiation ambient on the sensor from the test source (see Reference 7-G-15, -16)

The computer uses these inputs and a complex set of instructions to calculate the locations and values of the various radiation measurements. In substance, it does the following:

1. From the satellite position and attitude, it calculates where a line along the spin axis would intersect the earth. This is equivalent to the determination of the picture center required for location of the picture data.

a. Using only the satellite position (i.e., the point where a vertical from the satellite intersects the earth), Dr. Suomi of the University of Wisconsin can reduce the data from his omni-directional radiometer.

b. The intersection of the spin-axis with earth is the central point of each medium resolution radiometer measurement. The radiation measured is computed from the calibration and ancillary radiometer temperature data.

2. Considering only data from the scanning five-channel radiometer, the computer uses the earth intersection of the spin-axis, and the fact that the radiometer looks at an angle of 45° to the spin axis, to compute the scan of the radiometer along the earth.

3. From the rate of rotation of the satellite, and the sky-to-earth horizon crossing, where the radiometer value suddenly increases from 4°K to above 200°K, the computer calculates when and where along the scanning arc each observation was taken. This locates each data point geographically. The nadir angle of view is also calculated since this determines the amount of the atmosphere through which the radiation passed.

4. For each location, the measured radiation is now calculated using the recorded sensor value, calibration data, applicable ancillary data such as the radiometer temperature,

and the calibration information provided by the radiometer looking at the near absolute zero temperature of outer space.

5. The computer records these outputs on magnetic tape (the Final Meteorological Radiation or FMR tape). The tabulation on the tape includes the following information:

Time of Observation

Location of Point Observed (latitude and longitude)

Location of Satellite at time of Observation (latitude, longitude, and height)

Nadir Angle of View

Observed Radiation in each of the five channels

Solar Position (calculated during the processing and of value when studying reflected solar radiation data.)

The Final Meteorological Radiation Tape is the primary record for storage and research use of the TIROS radiation data. It is used as an input for further processing of the data on high speed computers. The FMR tape and such a computer can be used to print out ordinary tabulations of the data for manual study and research. The sheer bulk of the data—several hundred thousand values per orbit—makes it inexpedient to prepare such printed tabulations except for selected samples. For extensive use, high-speed computation is a must.

To avoid restricting use of the data solely to those with such equipment, one further presentation has been prepared for selected cases. Using again the FMR tape and a machine mapping program developed by the USWB for numerical weather predictions, the data can be printed out in their proper geographic location (see Figure 7-6, lower left). Selections of such plotted radiation data, contour-analyzed by the computing machine, have been distributed by NASA to research scientists. (see References 7-3, 7-4).

8

The Use of TIROS Data in Weather Analysis and Forecasting

TIROS I was the first satellite to provide data that could immediately be put to practical use—for weather analysis and forecasting. As soon as the first TIROS data were received at the Belmar, N. J., CDA station, the clouds were located by the hand procedures described in Chapter 7. These neph-analyses (cloud analyses) were sent by facsimile to the National Meteorological Center. For the first two-and-a-half days, there was sufficient doubt as to their accuracy, especially as regards geographical location of the clouds, to make it undesirable to further disseminate and use them. It is rumored unofficial use in practical weather analysis and forecasting was made in Hawaii on the first day, using the data received at Kaena Point. Finally, still less than 60 hours after launch, Col. (then Major) James B. Jones of the Air Weather Service and Cmdr. John Mirabito, of the Naval Weather Service, decided a nephanalysis for Europe and the Mediterranean, then less than four hours old, was reliable, and it was distributed by wire and radio facsimile to U. S. Air Weather Service and Navy meteorologists in the United States and overseas. This first historic nephanalysis is shown in Figure 8-1. Col. Jones was aided in his decision by the clearly identifiable land features along the coast of North Africa, which helped to locate the cloud data.

Since then, there has seldom been a day when a working TIROS was in orbit that one or more nephanalyses have not been disseminated to meteorologists over most of the world. Over the next four years, over 9,000 nephanalyses were sent out, and the total grows at a rate of about four hundred a month.

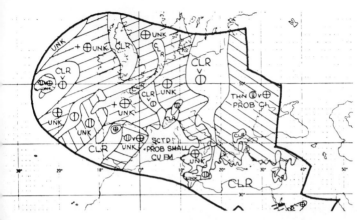

Fig. 8-1. The first operationally used TIROS nephanalysis (cloud analysis). (USAF)

With this much data being analyzed and distributed, and considering the costs of obtaining them, it is logical to ask what practical use is made of the data. (It cost over $15 million to develop, build, test, launch and operate TIROS I. Successive TIROS have cost about $4 million each: $1 million to build and test the spacecraft, $2.5 for the Thor-Delta and its launch support, and $0.5 million to run the data acquisition stations.)

Perhaps the most spectacular achievement of the TIROS data has been the discovery and/or tracking of over one hundred hurricanes and typhoons through the end of 1964. "Esther (1961) is the storm that will go down in history as the first hurricane ever discovered by a meteorological satellite." (see Reference 8-G-8). "On September 10, a vortex which was the formative stages of Esther was seen by TIROS to the west of the Cape Verde Islands at 11° N, 30° W." (The TIROS pictures and nephanalysis for this situation, from Reference 8-G-3, are shown in Figures 8-2 and 8-3.) "San Juan and Miami (USWB weather stations) were notified. On September 11, the magnitude of the cloud patterns indicated probable hurricane intensity and another advisory was transmitted to Miami. By September 12, the storm had for the first

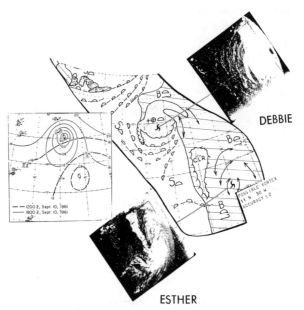

DEBBIE

ESTHER

Fig. 8-2. Nephanalysis, selected TIROS pictures, and section of the standard surface analysis on September 10, 1961, when hurricane Esther was first discovered. (USWB)

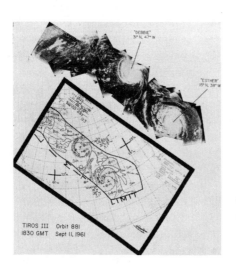

Fig. 8-3. Nephanalysis and mosaic of pictures on September 11, 1961, showing hurricanes Debbie and Esther about 24 hours later than the data in Fig. 8-2. (USWB)

time moved far enough to the west for aircraft reconnaissance. Based on the confirmation provided by these aircraft reports, Bulletin No. 1 on Hurricane Esther was issued by the Weather Bureau at San Juan at 6 Atlantic Standard Time, September 12. The first satellite data had been available nearly 48 hours earlier than these first aircraft data but, because the satellite has no way to measure exact wind intensity, were not by themselves sufficient to justify designating the storm a hurricane." Subsequent research, by Mr. Earl Merritt of ARACON Geophysics Company, suggests that the appearance of a cirrus (high ice crystal cloud) shield over the cloud bands indicates the attainment of hurricane winds (70 knots or greater). Based on this, the picture of Esther in Figure 8-2 indicates Esther had probably reached hurricane intensity before the time of the September 11 observation.

"TIROS coverage of Esther continued for nearly two weeks. The Air Weather Service has reported that on September 20 (1961) the TIROS pictures defined the southern and eastern extent of the cloud coverage associated with Esther where other data was sparse; very valuable data for briefing the staff of SAC's 8th Air Force on Hurricane Esther were provided. Still later, on September 24, due to the lack of pilot and ship reports around Esther, the data from Orbit No. 1063 helped define the extent of clouds around Esther. These data formed the basis for analyses which assisted in locating Esther's eye (central clear area) and in advising units of SAC's 8th Air Force with regard to mission planning."

Meanwhile, TIROS III was giving an equally impressive performance in the Pacific (see Reference 8-G-8); the case of Typhoon Sally. "On September 22 (1961), tropical depression No. 29 had been dropped from the maps after reconnaissance aircraft had found no further evidence of a storm circulation. On September 24, however, the Joint Typhoon Warning Center was advised of TIROS sightings of an apparent circulation in the area where depression No. 29 had last been seen. Aircraft were dispatched to investigate and on September 25 Bulletin No. 5 warned of regeneration and the birth of Typhoon Sally. A message of thanks and requests for further fixes on tropical storm Sally was received from Manila, P. I., in acknowledgment of a special U. S. Weather Bureau message sent on September 25, 1961. And the Japanese Meteorological Agency wired:

"ATTENTION: CHIEF, U. S. WEATHER BUREAU:

THANK YOU FOR YOUR TELEGRAM OF 25 0536 A.M. U.S. GOVERNMENT PD POSITION OF TROPICAL DE-PRESSION 998 MBS WAS FIXED—PLEASE CONTINUE TO SEND US TROPICAL VORTEX INFORMATION."

TIROS I provided international assistance ten days after launch, when a typhoon was observed north of New Zealand. Although its presence was already known to Australian meteorologists, the data that were radioed to Australia pro-vided further details on the position and extent of the storm.

On June 1, 1960, "a scheduled BOMARC firing (from Eglin AFB) was about to be scrubbed for lack of data over the Gulf range." (see Reference 8-G-6). "At the last moment, a TIROS (I) nephanalysis facsimile transmission arrived covering the range area. Maj. Brent F. Walker, Commander of the Eglin AFB Weather Detachment, hustled over to the range control with the information, and the firing was able to go ahead on schedule." In other cases, TIROS I data were cited as:

". . . very useful in preparation and verification of air refueling forecasts . . ."

"aided in forecast for recovery bases . . ."

". . . Forecast Center Commander states that the detailed analysis of cloud cover associated with systems approaching his refueling areas provided by TIROS enabled him to arrive at a more accurate forecast . . ."

". . . forecast accuracy . . . for the North Atlantic area . . . was enhanced . . . by virture of the detailed analysis provided by TIROS . . ."

An excellent example of the practical value of the data (again a TIROS I case), even close to the United States where weather data is not usually considered sparse, is shown in Figure 8-4. Figure 8-4 illustrates both conventional (within hatched edge) and TIROS data for cloud cover over the Atlantic Ocean just to the east of Florida, Georgia and Carolina for approximately midnight of May 8, 1960. Conventional data indicated an inverted U-shaped pattern of cloudiness with one long finger just to the east of the coast, an area of clear skies just to the east of this finger, and then another finger extending not quite so far south farther east. TIROS data for about the same time but not used by the analyst indicated that the central area was actually far from clear. Not only did the major area of cloudiness extend about 400 miles farther south than the conventional data suggested, but there were considerable broken cloudiness and cloud streaks, in patterns typical of a dissipating major storm system, throughout the supposedly clear area. The importance of the increased accuracy now available from such TIROS observations can be judged when it is noted that certain refueling areas of SAC are located within the area of Figure 8-4.

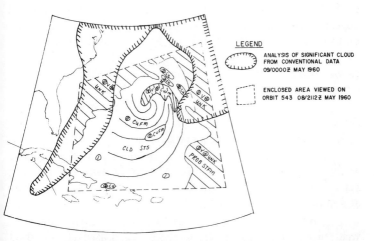

Fig. 8-4. Analysis of the cloud cover over the Atlantic Ocean just to the east of Florida for approximately 0000Z, May 9, 1960, showing increased detail and accuracy provided by TIROS as compared to conventional data. (USAF)

The first U. S. civilian use of TIROS data in the National Meteorological Center was on May 20, 1960 (see Reference 8-G-1). "NMC analysts used the TIROS Observation of the storm center" near the International Date Line to position the associated 500 mb (18,000 foot altitude) low center.

Although somewhat handicapped by the degraded data from its wide angle camera (see Chapter 5), TIROS II lost no time in becoming a worthy successor. "On November 30, 1960 (a week after launch) the surface maps for the Mediterranean area indicated frontolysis (dissipation) of a cold front which had entered the area from the Atlantic." (see Reference 8-G-1). However, "a nephanalysis from TIROS II indicated an almost continuous overcast band of cloud across the Mediterranean. On the basis of the TIROS observation, the cold front was reinstated on the surface chart and route forecasts were amended to include thunderstorm activity along the front. Air crews debriefed after flying from Athens to Tripoli verified the existence of the front and associated thunderstorms."

"Data from TIROS II which reached Australian forecasters in Melbourne (see Reference 8-G-1) was given credit for an assist in forecasting the break in a heat wave which preceded the New Year's holiday of 1961."

"Late in December (see Reference 8-G-4), southern Australia, including the city of Melbourne, was sweltering in one of its hottest spells in history, with temperatures over 100°. With the new year approaching, the citizens of Melbourne, as well as the Australian Bureau of Meteorology, were particularly eager to know whether cooler weather could be expected. On December 28, the Australians received from the U. S. Weather Bureau an analysis of cloud-cover pictures taken that day by the TIROS satellite over the Indian and South Pacific Oceans to the south of Australia. This showed a long band of clouds stretching from northwest to southeast over the ocean area to the west of Tasmania, which meant that a cold front was moving up toward Australia. On the basis of this analysis, the Australian Weather Service forecast that there would be a break in the heat wave shortly before

New Year. To the relief of the public, and the Australian weatherman, the cold front arrived exactly when forecast, with temperatures dropping 30°. The incident points up the great value of weather satellites in providing weather data over vast areas, particularly oceans, where observations cannot now be obtained on a regular basis. William J. Gibbs, assistant director of the Australian Bureau of Meteorology, said the satellite 'helped locate the cold front much more accurately than would otherwise have been possible,' since there are few weather observations in the ocean area to the south of Australia."

TIROS II contributed to many operational weather analyses. Samples (from Reference 8-G-7) are cited below:

"The cloud shield (observed by TIROS II) on one occasion definitely suggested a frontal wave position between Bermuda and the West Indies which was entered on the analyses and later confirmed as it passed to the southeast of Bermuda."

On January 30, 1961, TIROS data for an area of vital concern to the Albuquerque USWB station, Baja California, showed "that the cloud area over our part of the country was much more extensive than could be determined from our usual surface observations and weather charts."

On January 14, 1961, the Weather Bureau Airport Station, Honolulu, based a cloud forecast for one area "largely on our interpretation of the TIROS pictures."

"Summary of Orbit 143 was a better description of major cloud patterns over the Mediterranean than could be derived from available synoptic reports."

Several cases of the use of TIROS III data have already been cited. A few other striking cases (see Reference 8-G-8), from the many that exist, are summarized below:

"In one case (September 6, 1961) a squall line extending from Lake Huron to western Texas was discovered in TIROS photographs and entered on the surface chart on this evidence. This was a case where conventional observations over even a dense network failed to uncover a severe weather situation." This case is discussed in detail in Reference 8-G-3, and a TIROS picture of this squall line is shown in Figure 3-2.

The area in the eastern Pacific off Baja California "is extremely deficient in weather reports but, because of extensive fishing operations, of great commercial significance." On July 19 (1961) the position of tropical storm Liza in this area was moved 4° of latitude (over 250 miles) on the surface charts to agree with TIROS III pictures. On July 23, "Another nephanalysis showed a large but weak vortex— This may be the remains of tropical storm Liza which was (last) seen three days earlier. This storm has been dropped from analysis in the meantime, but on this information—the current analysis was altered to show an inverted trough over that area. This vortex position and related essentials were given to the San Francisco office via facsimile phone."

"In this same eastern Pacific area, on July 20, a tropical depression, Madeline, was observed by TIROS III. Tropical depression advisory No. 4, based solely on the satellite pictures, was issued by the Weather Bureau office in San Francisco (and) proved to be especially valuable to the tuna fishing fleet that operates off the coast of Mexico and southern California."

Moving to the North Atlantic, on September 10, 1961, ". . . the TIROS depiction of cloud distribution and organization associated with (hurricane) Debbie . . . was excellent and of great value . . . planners, controllers, and weathermen . . . were able to 'see' Debbie and reroute aircraft around the area. Earlier flights had encountered severe turbulence but the depiction of bands on the TIROS nephanalysis (cloud analysis) identified areas of probable convective activity and subsequent flights were rerouted to avoid these areas."

On August 24, 1961, TIROS data "assisted in forecasts for flights down range from Cape Canaveral."

"On September 19, the TIROS observations were: 'Very useful in briefing (SAC) reflex missions across the Atlantic.' "

Subsequent TIROS satellites have continued this record of operational achievements. For example (see Reference 8-G-2): "TIROS V had tropical storm Alma under surveillance once daily during Aug. 27-29, 1962. On each of these three days, selected photographs . . . were sent . . . to the National

Meteorological Center . . . (where, between August 27 and 28), they noted significant changes in the distribution of cloudy and clear areas near the storm center. These changes were among the factors which led to a forecast that the storm would gradually lose intensity. During the subsequent 24-48 hours the storm weakened as forecast."

Pilots flying the Atlantic from Idlewild International Airport, New York, have been enthusiastic about TIROS data. The supervisory forecaster there has stated, with regard to TIROS III data (see Reference 8-G-9): "A copy of the depiction (TIROS nephanalysis) was used in lieu of any weather depiction form normally prepared" for the route between New York and Dakar, Africa. "The response from crew members on (the use and availability of these charts) has been enthusiastic. There is absolutely no question that the TIROS (charts) are an invaluable aid in our daily activities."

After using data based on TIROS IV observations, a Pan American Airlines pilot stated (see Reference 8-G-2): "Enclosed is the TIROS weather map given me on my departure (on May 4, 1962). . . . from 60° West (over the Atlantic) to Dakar (Africa), the map was so accurate as to be almost unbelievable. The map position of the cold front was not only located exactly, but with a 150-mile scan on radar its northeast-southwest positioning was clearly definable. The cloud amounts and types were completely correct. Continuing on the flight from (Dakar to Liberia), it too was letter perfect with the exception of our finding some 2/8 (cumulonimbus) off the coast—probably due to the morning buildup . . . In my estimation we have found the answer; let's send up more TIROS."

As any meteorologist will readily tell you, such praise of a weather forecast by a pilot is extremely rare and very hard to come by.

This litany of TIROS operational achievements could continue indefinitely. However, here is a summary of TIROS operational outputs and achievements (page 136):

"The Special storm advisories issued" line in the tabulation refers to a program begun with TIROS III and

Operational Uses of TIROS Data

	I	II	III	IV	V	VI	VII (Thru Dec. 1964)	VIII (Thru Dec. 1964)
Operationally useful pictures obtained	19,389	22,500	24,000	23,370	48,562	59,830	87,212	56,321
Nephanalyses (cloud analyses) prepared	333	455	755	836	1,851	2,162	3,624	2,720
Nephanalyses disseminated by facsimile	Unknown	305	744	795	1,787	2,097	3,544	2,602
Nephanalyses disseminated by teletype	Few	295	665	694	1,250	1,476	2,438	1,520
Special storm advisories issued	Unknown	Unknown	70	102	391	361	564	350
Suggested adjustments to conventional weather analyses	Unknown	Unknown	76 .	79	111	116	171	114
Frontal positions relocated				39	41	42	47	34
Frontal waves (developing storms) added or relocated				8	7	12	10	4
Surface pressure patterns adjusted				25	53	59	110	61
500 mb (18,000 ft) analyses adjusted				7	10	3	4	15
Number of hurricanes and typhoons observed	1	—	14	—	19	14	51	37
Number of separate days hurricanes and typhoons observed					66	42	181	104

continued. (see Reference 8-G-1). "When a previously unreported vortex (storm), or a vortex in a position significantly different from that on an existing analysis is seen, a directed (specifically addressed) message is sent to the forecasters whose area is most likely to be affected. A special message is used so that the information will be relayed as rapidly as possible." The special advisories dispatched during the useful life of TIROS V were:

International

Argentina	2
Australia	9
Brazil	3
British East African Territories	2
Burma	1
Ceylon	0
Chile	3
China (Formosa)	3
East Pakistan	1
Great Britain	2
Iceland	2
India	1
Ireland	2
Japan	3
Kenya	2
Malagasy Republic	9
Mauritius	13
Mexico	10
New Zealand	3
Nicaragua	1
Nigeria	2
Philippines	5
Portugal	2
Senegal	3
South Africa	4
Surinam	1
Uruguay	2
Venezuela	4
West Pakistan	0
Total	**95**

Weather Bureau

Atlanta	1
Boston	1
Guam	1
Honolulu	22
Kansas City	1
Los Angeles	17·
Miami	17
New Orleans	4
New York	1
St. Louis	1
San Francisco	24
San Juan	16
Seattle	1
Total	**107**

USAF Detachments

Guam	55
Honolulu	55
Lajes, Azores	2
Tokyo	55
Total	**167**

USN Weather Centrals

Alameda, California	9
Pearl Harbor, Hawaii	11
Port Lyautey, Morocco	2
Total	**22**

Many of these locations also were sent special advisories based on data from previous and/or subsequent TIROS. In addition to the places listed, many other countries have also been furnished advisories based on data from previous and/or subsequent TIROS; weather conditions just did not happen to merit sending advisories to them during the life of the TIROS V.

TIROS data have also been used to provide support particularly tailored to a great number of special civilian and military operational, research, and space projects, some of which are tabulated below:

Projects Supported

		II	III	IV	V	VI	VII	VIII
					TIROS			
Project Mercury			x	2	x	x		
Ranger (NASA Lunar Probe)			x	x			x	x
Discoverer (USAF Satellite)			x	x				
Long Tom (Australian Meteorological Rocket)			x	x				
U.S. Navy Operations and Projects			x		x	x	x	x
Satellite Sea Ice Reconnaissance		x		x	x	x	x	x
Joint Task Force 8 (Atomic Tests)				x	x			
California Water Survey (Snow cover observations)			x					
USAF Operations & Projects				3	6	7	x	x
University Research Projects				2	x	x	x	x
Illinois State Water Survey					x			
Mariner Launch (NASA Venus Probe)					x			
NASA Scout Launches					x			
International Indian Ocean Expedition					x	x	x	x
U.S. Army Operations & Projects					x	x		
Equatorial Atlantic Oceanography Research					x	x	x	x
Antarctic Resupply Mission			x	x	x	x	x	

With regard to the Antarctic Resupply Mission support, Mace and Jones (see Reference 8-G-1) have noted: "During certain periods, excellent coverage of the area between Australia-New Zealand and the Antarctic is obtained. At these times the nephanalysis charts for this area are transmitted by (radio) facsimile by the U. S. Navy directly to the station at McMurdo Sound, Antarctica. This information is used to forecast for the resupply missions to Antarctica."

9

Research Use of TIROS Data and the Results Obtained

In Chapter 8, we discussed the current analysis and forecasting use of the TIROS data. Here, we will examine some of the work that is being done with TIROS data to improve our weather analysis capabilities as well as to accumulate further knowledge of our universe.

The first TIROS-observed atmospheric features to attract great scientific interest were the large and vivid spiral cloud vortices. Prior to the launch of TIROS there had been considerable discussion as to whether such spiral patterns existed and, if they did, whether they would be visible. By the time TIROS I had completed its first day in orbit, there were no longer doubts as to the existence and visibility of these patterns; discussion now centers on the still unresolved problems of how they are created, and how they should be interpreted both theoretically and practically (see Reference 14-36).

Over 100 years ago and long before the advent of aircraft, let alone satellites, spiral storm patterns had been visualized by the astute mind of Admiral Fitz Roy, the first chief of the British Meteorological Office (see References 9-1, -2). The resemblance of Fitz Roy's concept to those patterns seen by TIROS is striking.

A further point of interest is the great geometric similarity between the spiral cloud patterns seen by TIROS and patterns seen in the spiral nebulae or island universes which populate the infinite reaches of space.

While there are striking similarities between many of the TIROS-observed spirals and those of the galaxies, there are also major differences. The most obvious is size; the TIROS spirals are no more than 2,000 miles in diameter, while the galaxies have diameters of about 100,000 light years. A light year is some 5.88×10^{12} (nearly six trillion) miles, so the ratio of diameters is about six hundred trillion to one.

A more fundamental difference is that the vortices in our atmosphere are responsive to the laws of hydrodynamics, while the spiral nebula obey magneto-dynamic or hydromagnetic laws. In hydrodynamics, the basic principle is Newton's Law of Motion ($F = Ma$), with the forces being gravity, friction, and pressure. In hydromagnetics, there are not only Newton's Law and these forces, but also Maxwell's electromagnetic equations and electromagnetic forces to be taken into account. Furthermore, due to the size of the galaxies and the relative velocities of the stars within them, there are probably relativistic effects of some consequence. These are effects that become apparent as velocities approach the speed of light.

Nevertheless, because of the striking geometric similarity, it seems almost certain that there exist more fundamental analogies that, when understood, may help to explain why nature so often chooses spiral patterns; they are common in biology, as shown by such diverse aspects as common sea shells and the DNA molecules that determine our very beings.

Many of the earliest research papers resulting from the TIROS data were based on studies of spiral cloud patterns. Bristor and Ruzecki (see Reference 9-3) studied a well-developed storm over the central United States, relating the clear and cloud-covered areas to, respectively, the cold-dry air behind and the warm-moist air ahead of a cold front. Fritz (see Reference 9-4) showed that a similar relationship existed in a mature storm over the Atlantic even after the two air masses had circulated completely around the storm center. Winston and Tourville (see Reference 9-5) and Winston (see Reference 9-6) analyzed storms in the Gulf of Alaska and the subtropical eastern North Pacific; in both cases, they found the satellite pictures provided significant new data on fronts and vertical air motions.

These and other studies of such spiral cloud vortex cases lacked an essential ingredient: Each dealt with a separate case and it was difficult to extract generalizations applicable to other situations. The first published attempt at such generalizations was that of Boucher and Newcomb (see Reference 9-2). They studied the similarities and differences among some 30 vortex cases observed by TIROS I.

Many major extra-tropical storms develop as growth, occlusion and dissipation of a wave on a front. This sequence, a foundation of modern meteorology, was discovered by Bjerknes and Solberg in the early 1920's (see Reference 9-7). Boucher and Newcomb related various cloud vortex patterns to stages of wave development and cyclone formation. Starting with a wave on the front, the cold air poleward and to the rear (westward) of the storm penetrates deeper and deeper until it has circulated completely around the storm center and is finally so intermixed with the other air masses that no dividing lines can be discerned. At this point, with cold air underlying the warmer air in all places, energy available from the difference in density of the heavy cold versus the light warm air has been used, and the storm dies as friction gradually slows its winds. Some of the cloud patterns accompanying this sequence of developments are illustrated in Fig. 1-17 (see Reference 9-56; 9-G-6).

Studies of storm development based on the Boucher-Newcomb model by Merritt of ARACON Geophysics Company, the author, and many others are continuing. Merritt has applied the model to analysis and forecasting for the vast oceanic areas just off the Antarctic continent, where satellites often provide the only available data (see Reference 9-8). His results will be of significant value in forecasting for Antarctic resupply programs (see Reference 14-36).

At Stanford Research Institute, Nagle, Serebreny, and their colleagues (see References 9-9, 1-6) have studied storm systems of the North Pacific Ocean. In one case they discovered a small spiral cloud pattern, to the west of a dissipating major cyclone, which was not revealed by any data other than the TIROS pictures. A day later, this small vortex caused heavy rains along the Washington coast. Both research and practical experience with the TIROS data have suggested that spiral cloud formations should always be watched as potential (although far from inevitable) sources of heavy rain; the seriously flooding rains that caused much damage and loss of lives in Spain in 1962 came from a storm with a spiral pattern.

A second feature in the early TIROS pictures that drew great attention was patterns of cells. Such cellular patterns are too large to be seen from a single weather station or aircraft, too small to be detected by a network of stations; but from their frequent appearance in TIROS pictures, particularly in the cold air to the rear of a major storm, they play a major role in convection and the vertical redistribution of moisture and heat over the oceans. Superfically, they appear like cells, detected by and named for Bénard, in fluids heated from below such as a pan of water just prior to boiling. But, from both theory and measurement, Bénard cells should have a specific ratio of height to diameter. As Kreuger and Fritz (see Reference 9-10) showed, these TIROS-observed cells have diameters about ten times too large (for reasonable estimates of their heights) to fit the theory of Bénard's cells. Many research groups beside Fritz and his colleagues (see Reference 9-G-3) have investigated this intriguing problem of the cells that appeared to be ten times larger than theory said they could be. Perhaps, like the famous story of the bumble-bee whose flight was supposed to violate all laws of aeronautical engineering, the cells have never read the theory and so continue on their way. Among these groups are those of Sasaki (see Reference 9-11) and Scorer (see Reference 9-12). Scorer (see Reference 9-13) has calculated that the effects of temperature gradients and wind shears in the atmosphere, not duplicated in the pans of fluid in which Bérnard cells have been studied, are sufficient to explain the apparent discrepancy in the ratio. Whether the problem has been solved by this hypothesis remains to be established but, in any event, these TIROS observations have done much to increase our understanding of convective processes in the atmosphere. Merritt and Rogers (see Reference 9-8) have discovered some very useful relationships between the cell patterns, and the speed and direction of the wind. From these, wind analyses over the data-sparse ocean areas can be improved.

One of the very real problems that has faced users of TIROS data has been identification of the cloud types from the features in the pictures. In wide angle camera pictures, the available resolution is too gross to reproduce the small scale cloud forms on which identification of cloud type from the ground is based. The problem is complicated by a psychological quirk—a tendency that must be constantly overcome, even by experts, to look at a TIROS picture and think "I remember seeing a cloud like that up in the sky last week." This is seldom true since the area of the sky one can see from a single location on the ground is seldom as great as 1,000 square miles, whereas the area of TIROS pictures is about 500 times as great. Accordingly, cloud features seen in TIROS pictures are at least 10 to 100 times the size of those seen from the ground.

In anticipation of these problems, special ground observations, high altitude aircraft photographs of clouds, radar data, and other comparative measurements were obtained concurrent with the overflights of TIROS. This program, started before TIROS I was launched, was expanded for subsequent TIROS. For TIROS II and III, in particular, foreign as well as United States concurrent observations were encouraged, as will be discussed in Chapter 13. For later TIROS, the pupils of a number of schools near Washington, D. C., and in other places, have cooperated by making cloud observations about the times TIROS was expected to be photographing their area.

While the problems of cloud identification are far from solved, considerable progress has been made in finding characteristics of the clouds in the pictures (shape, brightness, texture, edge sharpness, etc.) from which the cloud types can be deduced with confidence. Leaders in this program of research have been Conover of the Air Force Cambridge Research Laboratories (see References 9-14, -15, -G-1) and Erickson and Hubert of the USWB (see Reference 9-16, -G-5). The procedures they have developed are rather involved, and it is sufficient here to summarize them as Fritz (see Reference 9-G-2) has done: ". . . resolution, contrast and brightness (are) among the factors in detecting cloud characteristics.

Almost all cloud patterns are observable. Cumuliform and stratiform cloud patterns appear as spiral arrays, cloud streets, and cellular patterns; these cloud forms appear also in waves, vortices, and other atmospheric phenomena. Cirrus and alto-stratus are sometimes evident in fibrous form. But thin cirrus clouds, especially when scattered, are not seen by the TIROS cameras. Fields of small, scattered fair weather cumulus were also not discernible as such. . . ."

Early in this research it became apparent that cloud identification was further complicated by geologic and geographic features often mistaken for clouds. These include snow on mountains, ice-covered lakes, sun glints off water surfaces, and bright desert sands.

Dark features, such as lakes, may appear to be breaks in thin or hazy cloud cover. To aid meteorologists in identifying such features, Cronin (see Reference 9-17) has prepared a map and descriptive report of terrestrial features seen by TIROS over the United States.

The non-meteorological features observed by TIROS are not solely a handicap, as has been discussed by Singer and Popham (see Reference 9-18). Detection of forest fires and of locust swarms have been suggested as possible applications. Snow observations can provide data on the water which will become available for use, both for power and irrigation, as the snows melt. Sun glints (reflections) provide information on the state of the sea and the accompanying winds; small bright spots denote the mirror-like reflections of calms, whereas diffuse, less-brilliant glints denote rougher water and stronger winds. The writer, on an evening flight into San Francisco, noted a vivid demonstration of this effect. Bright moon-glints were seen on the calm surfaces of irrigation canals near Oakland. But, over San Francisco Bay, the wind roughened the water and it was hard to find any reflection of the moon.

The most investigated non-meteorological use has been in the Gulf of the St. Lawrence (see References 9-19, -20, -33). Ice floes there were noted in TIROS I pictures the day it was launched (see Reference 9-21). A TIROS II picture of ice in that region is shown in Chapter 1. Ice distributions in this area are vital to economic ship navigation, especially in the late winter and early spring. Satellites can provide far greater coverage, although less detail, than any economically feasible number of aircraft. A team effort of satellites and reconnaissance aircraft may be ideal for this purpose, with the satellites providing the large scale picture while the aircraft can be dispatched, on the basis of the satellite data, to provide more detail of the more critical areas. (see Reference 3-1).

Even geologists and geographers are finding TIROS data of significant research value. As in the case of clouds, satellites can record terrestrial features too large to be observed from the ground or aircraft, but sufficiently small to be missed in regular map analyses. (see Reference 9-33). Professor Bird of McGill University, Montreal, Canada, using TIROS data, has detected some land features over Africa, of this scale of size, which seem to defy explanation on the basis of presently available data for their area (see NASA Report CR-98).

Moving from ground levels to that of the tropopause (some 30,000 to 40,000 feet in altitude), research by such workers as Conover (see Reference 9-14) and Merritt (see Reference 9-22) has shown that TIROS data can be used to identify jet streams, the narrow bands of very strong winds which can speed an aircraft on its way (usually when the flight is to the east) or slow it severely when it fights head winds. The identifying features are long bands of cirrus clouds, found parallel to and just equatorward of the core of the jet stream. A jet stream related cirrus cloud band, over southern Egypt and the northern Red Sea, can be seen in Figure 9-1.

TIROS cloud patterns can also provide data on wind flows at lower levels, at times for cases not readily observable by other means. Examples include lee wave clouds and vortex disturbances in the lee of subtropical islands. These lee vortices, first noted by Bowley, *et al* (see Reference 9-23) and later more fully studied by Hubert and Krueger (see Reference 1-4), are yet to be fully explained. The satellite is again playing the dual role of both increasing our knowledge and revealing our deficiencies: The vortices reveal air motions of

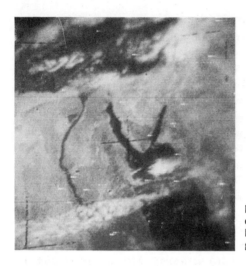

Fig. 9-1. Jet stream cirrus bands over the Red Sea. (TIROS photograph)

which we were previously unaware; the deficiencies are our current inability to account for them. Research on this problem will almost certainly further our understanding of turbulence and small scale atmospheric motions and, ultimately, our ability to forecast weather in the small scale.

Some of the most valuable data provided by TIROS have been for tropical regions. Meteorological research (and weather forecasting) in tropical areas is made difficult by the sparsity of data over vast ocean areas; the problems are intensified by a reduced level of technological development in many of the land areas. To complicate things further, a major analytical tool, the field of pressure, is of greatly degraded value. Not only are tropical pressure changes normally slight, but, due to the effects of the earth's rotation on the winds approaching zero at the equator, the approximate balance between wind and pressure gradient, so common in temperate regions, ceases to be applicable. As a consequence, extrapolation of pressure analyses into areas lacking in observations are of limited value in the tropics.

The consequences of this lack of data are illustrated by a single example: The vigorous arguments still raging, after more than twenty years, as to the reality and significance of the so-called *Easterly Waves*, first proposed by Dunn (see Reference 9-24) in 1940 and more fully explored by Riehl (see Reference 9-25). Their role as a possible source of Atlantic Hurricanes is still hotly debated. TIROS pictures of Easterly Waves, studied by Merritt (see Reference 9-53), have helped considerably toward resolving these arguments.

A second example is provided by Sadler (see Reference 9-26), who showed from TIROS I observations that a tropical storm, believed to have dissipated over the Arabian Sea, had penetrated some 300 miles into Arabia itself.

Although pressure data are of reduced value in the tropics, wind direction is critical. Most tropical weather is produced by winds flowing over mountainous islands, or by the upward motions resulting from converging air streams. While the satellite cannot see the winds, certain aspects of the flow can be deduced from the cloud patterns, which clearly depict the windward sides of land masses and the critical regions of convergence. Hubert (see References 9-27, -28) has studied these convergence lines, stating in one case: ". . . although this synoptic system was vigorous and well documented by the (TIROS) pictures, its existence and extent cannot be delineated by standard meteorological observations." Schuetz and Fritz (see Reference 9-29) have studied the use of cloud streets (parallel lines of cumulus clouds) as indicators of the wind direction, and the sources of error in such applications.

The most critical tropical weather system is, of course, the hurricane in the North Atlantic, and its counterparts, the typhoon in the Pacific and the Tropical Cyclone in the Indian Ocean. The use of TIROS data in detecting and forecasting these storms was discussed in Chapter 8. Considerable research is being directed toward improving our understanding of these storms and our techniques for forecasting their movement and severity. Merritt (see Reference 9-30) and Fritz (see Reference 9-31) have independently used TIROS data to confirm earlier suspicions that many North Atlantic Hurricanes form from African disturbances (see References 9-24, -25). Merritt (see References 9-32, -53) has proposed a model of tropical storm development, analogous to the cyclonic storm model for temperature latitudes developed by Boucher and Newcomb. From this model, the stage, intensity, and wind velocity in a tropical storm, cyclone, hurricane, or typhoon can be deduced. The appearance of a cirrus cloud veil over the earlier appearing cyclonic banding is indicative of the attainment of hurricane force winds—those exceeding 70 mph.

Sadler has shown that tropical storms in the Eastern Pacific, off Baja California, are far more frequent than data from sources other than TIROS have led us to believe (see Reference 9-54). Some of these storms, although with reduced intensity, move far westward into the Pacific, influencing the weather at such distant islands as Palmyra and Johnston, near the International Date Line. However, care must be taken when analyzing TIROS pictures to distinguish between these low level vortices and other cyclonic cells in the upper tropospheric tropical troughs, which are also "important cloud and weather-producing systems." An "upper cell . . . located over the northern Gulf of Mexico, was not detectable in the synoptic analyses at 10,000 feet and below, yet it produced widespread precipitation, thunderstorms, and squalls over the Gulf."

A particularly significant Sadler study dates back to his analyses of the cloud pictures from the Atlas 11c (see Reference 4-14) and led him to propose an entirely new pattern of the tropical upper level general circulation (the large scale, average wind patterns and flows). TIROS pictures and other data showed these "circulation patterns are not properly depicted in most upper wind statistics and analysis charts of the northern hemisphere" (see Reference 9-26) and that the average trough and ridge patterns, instead of having an east-west orientation, are helixes (spirals) curving poleward as one goes along them from west to east. We obviously still have a great deal to learn about the tropical portion of our atmosphere, and the tropics cover some fifty per cent of the earth. Consideration is being given to placing weather satellites in equatorial orbits to insure adequate coverage of this important area.

Research analyses of TIROS data are also providing new

insights into the true meanings of other meteorological observations. One such case illustrates how scientific research may at times fail its intended purpose, but, concurrently, provide unforeseen results of a possibly more valuable nature.

During the mid-1950's, Dr. M. G. H. Ligda, then at Texas A & M and now with Stanford Research Institute (SRI), suggested to the author that it might be of considerable value to obtain a set of radar observations coincident with cloud pictures taken from one of the White Sands research rockets. Dr. Ligda was at the time collecting and studying weather radar data from a wide network of stations. Unfortuntely, it was never possible to coordinate properly the two types of observations. When planning for the utilization of TIROS data, the idea was revived with a more specific objective: Could clouds with rain or snow falling from them be identified from the TIROS pictures? The radar data would indicate where precipitation was falling. Dr. Ligda and his colleagues at SRI were asked to gather radar data from a large network of both ground and airborne stations and to jointly analyze these data and those from the TIROS (see References 9-34, -35, -36, -37).

The immediate results were discouraging. Moderate or heavier precipitation was usually found to be restricted to areas of bright clouds (the brightness indicating relatively thick cloudiness) or to areas with vortex cloud patterns, but large areas of bright clouds and vortex patterns had no corresponding precipitation. Roland Nagle, who was now heading this particular project, was not satisfied with these initial and rather negative results. He used an old technique developed for applying radar data to estimating the amount of water, from rain, available for use as power or irrigation. In these applications, the radar scope is photographed with several hour time exposures, rather than as an instantaneous snapshot. This immediately revealed that the total area where precipitation had occurred at one time or another within a several hour period was highly correlated to the cloud pattern features and brighter areas (see Reference 9-37). Only a small fraction of a cloud area potentially capable of giving rain is apt to be doing so at any one time.

As a result, the value and ways of using radar data in meteorology have been fundamentally reconsidered. It is immediately apparent that the instantaneous radar precipitation patterns have value only over short distances and times, as for a squall line only a short distance away. To be useful in forecasting for larger areas and longer time periods the patterns integrated over periods of several hours should be used. The TIROS data have led to a new philosophy as to the ways to use a different observation—weather radar. As we will see in Chapter 14, these results have also had an impact on proposals for using radar as a satellite observing technique (see Reference 9-38).

Turning to the research that has been done with the radiometric measurements discussed in Chapter 6, progress here has been slowed by problems inherent to the reduction of these data to forms useful to the research worker. There are fewer results available that can be reviewed without getting into unduly technical matters. Radiation data can be expected to attain a significance at least approximating that of the cloud picture data; many meteorologists believe that their long term importance will exceed that of the cloud pictures (see Reference 14-36).

Use of the 8-12 micron "window" data to observe cloud cover at night has been based on the colder cloud top temperatures, as explained in Chapter 6. The first definitive results were reported by Fritz and Winston (see Reference 9-39). These and other subsequent studies (see References 9-40, -41, -42) have confirmed the infrared detection of cloud-covered areas, although there will inevitably be ambiguities in cases of very low clouds and less than complete overcasts.

Both Bandeen and his colleagues (see Reference 9-41) and Fujita and his associates (see Reference 9-43) have used TIROS radiation data to study cloud heights in Hurricane Anna. Bandeen showed that the temperatures measured by the TIROS window channel (which indicates the temperature at the cloud top) over Anna were *colder* than those measured by the 6.3 micron (water vapor) channel, which indicates the temperature of the water vapor above the cloud top. The significance of this is best stated by the authors themselves.

"The dramatic reversal of the usual order of equivalent black body temperatures over the hurricane, together with the low channel 2 ("window") measurement, suggests that the cloud tops over Anna were very high—probably near the height of the tropopause. The magnitude of the difference between the equivalent black body temperatures measured by channel 1 (6.3 micron water vapor) and channel 2 infer a very wet stratosphere with a sharp temperature inversion (increase of temperature with height) above the cloud tops."

Studies of the TIROS "window" data as applied to measurements of surface temperatures (see References 9-44, -45) have shown that surface temperatures, as deduced from the satellite measurements, appear somewhat colder, compared to their actual values, than would have been expected from radiation theory and current concepts of atmospheric composition and structure. This has led to the idea that there is more water vapor or dust in the high atmosphere than yet measured. There are other reasons, such as the comparatively rare observations of the extremely high noctilucent clouds (see Reference 9-46) to further sustain these suspicions.

A number of groups have been comparing the TIROS and other radiation measurements, over periods of several days or weeks, with calculated normal values of the gains and losses of atmospheric energy (see References 9-47, -48, -49, -50, -51). In general the correlations have been satisfactory, confirming the general accuracy and value of the TIROS data, and laying the foundation for further studies which will consider time and space variations of the atmospheric albedo and the outgoing long-wave radiation.

One problem in these studies is that the satellite measurement of the radiation reflected or emitted from a spot can usually be made only from one angle (on a particular orbit), whereas the total reflected or emitted radiation leaves the atmosphere at all angles from horizon to horizon. Radiation intensity varies with angle. These variations are closely related to the "limb-darkening" effect used by Mariner II to measure the surface temperature of Venus. Studies of these matters and of how to calculate total values from a single measurement have been made by Wexler (see Reference 9-44) and Wark and his colleagues (see Reference 9-45).

The above discussions give only a glimpse of studies of the TIROS data, the results obtained, and the present and foreseeable significance both practical and theoretical, of these results. Space, my ignorance, and the rapid rate of progress have all contributed to inevitable omissions. But it should be obvious that meterological satellite data will continue to be of great value in meteorological research. And, as quickly as these data add to our knowledge of the atmosphere, they raise new and equally vital questions; some of these questions will defy answering for many years.

10

Nimbus

Although TIROS has been of great value to meteorology, it has severe limitations. These derive from its inclined orbit and spin stabilization. Coverage of the earth is limited to latitudes equatorward of about 65° (see Figure 10-1), while the cameras point toward the earth only one-fourth to one-third of each orbit. For reasons described in Chapter 12, TIROS cloud picture coverage is frequently not possible in one hemisphere or the other. In addition, the weight, space, and power permitted by TIROS limit the number, types, and capabilities of the sensors.

These limitations and the need to develop an improved meteorological satellite were recognized before the launch of TIROS I. The design of Nimbus was begun in late 1959. It included concepts proposed in 1957 by Touart and the author (see Reference 4-11) and incorporated in the 1958 Air Force proposal to the Advanced Research Project Agency. The data processing system includes concepts suggested by the author in 1960 (see Reference 10-2). But Nimbus was designed primarily by Dr. Rudolph Stampfl and his colleagues of NASA's Goddard Space Flight Center (see Reference 10-3). The name (the Latin word for cloud, now usually applied to rain-carrying clouds) (see Reference 10-G-1) was chosen by Mr. Edward Cortwright, then Chief, Advanced Technology Program, NASA Headquarters (see Reference 10-1).

The Nimbus objectives include: (1) a near-polar orbit to permit observation of the entire earth, and (2) earth-stabilization so that the cameras and other sensors could always point toward the earth (see Figure 10-1). The weight and orbit were chosen to be compatible with the Thor Agena B.

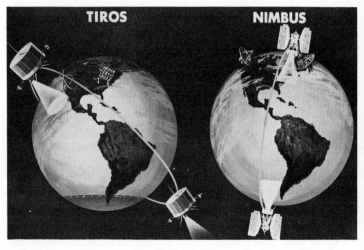

Fig. 10-1.   Comparison of TIROS and Nimbus coverage. (NASA)

As the design proceeded, the following additional concepts were incorporated:

(1) A retrograde (east-to-west) orbit, inclined about 80° to the equator. This permits the spacecraft to cross the equator at local noon (northbound) and local midnight (southbound) on every orbit (see Chapter 12). In the later Nimbus, other local times twelve hours apart may be chosen. This insures seeing the poles on each orbit, and the entire earth twice each day.

(2) An orbit altitude of about 1000 Km (600 nautical miles); high enough for overlapping coverage at the equator while avoiding the radiation in the Van Allen belts, which would damage solar cells and parts of the electronics.

(3) A modular (standard unit) construction, to allow for changes in later satellites.

(4) The base area kept clear for use of the earth-viewing sensors.

Nimbus is shown in Figure 10-2. Most of the subsystems are analogous to those in TIROS and will be discussed in turn.

Originally the Aeronomy and Meteorology (A&M) Division of the Goddard Space Flight Center planned to integrate and test the spacecraft. By early 1961, the A&M Division had awarded separate contracts for some fifteen subsystems. It was then decided to contract with General Electric's Missile and Space Vehicle Department, Valley Forge, Pa., for the structure, integration of the several subsystems, and qualification testing. During these initial stages, Mr. William Stroud, Director of the A&M Division, served as Project Manager. In late 1961, Mr. Harry Press became permanent Project Manager. Dr. Stampfl, the Spacecraft Systems Manager for the design phases, was succeeded first by Mr. J. V. Michaels and later by Mr. M. Schneebaum.

Shape and Structure

Nimbus consists of:

(1) A base Sensory Ring, in or on which are mounted the meteorological sensors, most of the electronics except the controls system, and the transmitting antennas. The ring is 57 inches in diameter and 13 inches high.

(2) The Control and Stabilization Subsystem, a separate turret-like structure.

(3) Trusses interconnecting the sensory ring and the controls section.

(4) Two solar paddles, each 96 inches by 38.5 inches, which turn on shafts extending from the controls section.

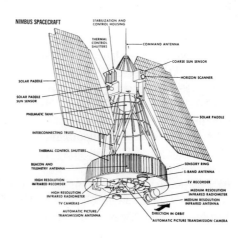

Fig. 10-2. The Nimbus spacecraft. (NASA)

(5) A command (receiving) antenna mounted on the controls section.

In orbit, as in Figure 10-2, with the paddles extended, the satellite is about eleven feet across and nine feet high. For launch, the paddles are folded within the launch vehicle.

The Nimbus structure must survive the launch stresses and maintain the accurate alignment of the sensors. The Nimbus configuration was also designed to meet other objectives:

(1) Due to the slight decrease of gravity with height (because gravitational attraction decreases with the square of the distance), a dumbbell-like array of two separated masses has a tendency to align its axis with the vertical. The same principle causes the moon to keep the same face toward the earth. The Nimbus sensory ring and the controls section provide the two masses and aid the controls system in keeping the spacecraft so the sensors point toward the earth.

(2) The open area inside the interconnecting truss provides access to the center of gravity of the spacecraft. The spacecraft can be balanced here on an "air-bearing" for testing of the controls subsystem. The "air-bearing" is a large ball, fitting into a bowl-like structure but separated from it by a stream of air, to which the spacecraft is attached to allow nearly frictionless movement of the ball and the attached spacecraft.

(3) Since the controls system and the sensory ring are essentially independent, relatively major modifications can be made in one part without requiring an extensive redesign of the other. Similarly, the sensory ring is a series of standard size or modular compartments, so that new or redesigned subsystems can be substituted from one Nimbus to another.

The following equipments are placed within the modules: Transmitter for AVCS cameras and the high resolution radiometer (HRIR); command clock; batteries and power subsystem electronics; command subsystem receiver, HRIR electronics; camera electronics for Automatic Picture Transmission (APT) camera (the difference between the AVCS and APT cameras will be discussed later); telemetry and beacon electronics; medium resolution radiometer electronics (not in Nimbus I), and AVCS electronics.

Although Figure 10-2 shows two sets of both AVCS and APT cameras, weight limitations permitted only one set of each in the first Nimbus.

(4) Because the controls and sensory sections are separate, the two sections can be considered independently when designing to maintain proper temperatures. Nimbus regulates the temperatures of the various systems by heat conduction, insulation, and radiating surfaces. In addition, the Nimbus controls system and sensory ring have sets of shutters that close to retain heat when too cool, and open when too warm. Thermostats and bellows move these shutters. In the event of a failure, a fail-safe bellows leaves the shutters at a half-open position. This temperature control system keeps the various Nimbus subsystems within $\pm$ 5°C of their design values.

Controls and Stablization Subsystem

Nimbus has earth stabilization, i.e., the base and sensors always point toward the earth, and the spacecraft always points forward along the orbit. The development of the controls system was difficult and critical. The contract for it to General Electric's Missile and Space Vehicle Department was the first to be awarded. This subsystem alone is more complex than an entire TIROS.

The Nimbus Control and Stabilization Subsystem performs three functions:

(1) Horizon sensors mounted on the front and rear of the Controls Subsystem turret scan, note departures from the vertical of the spacecraft axis, and using a computer, and flywheels and gas nozzles, correct any departures. Accordingly, the sensors on the base of the spacecraft can look straight down.

(2) Sun sensors, and later a gyroscope, sense whether the spacecraft is facing along the orbit. If not, another flywheel or gas jet corrects this. The camera views and radiometer scans are perpendicular to the path of the satellite for maximum coverage.

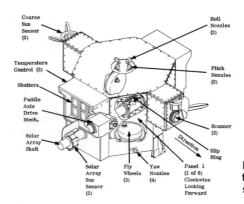

Fig. 10-3. A sketch of the Nimbus controls subsystem. (NASA)

(3) Other sun sensors, mounted on the paddle shafts (which protrude from the Controls turret) cause a motor to turn the shafts to keep the solar cells facing the sun and producing maximum power.

A sketch of the Nimbus Controls Subsystem, and some of its components, is shown in Figure 10-3.

It will be helpful to first define the set of axes normally used for spacecraft motions. As a carry-over from aeronautics, the

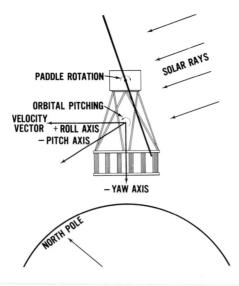

Fig. 10-4. Nimbus spacecraft axes. (NASA)

terms pitch, roll, and yaw are used. The axes are shown in Figure 10-4. Pitch is a nose-up or -down motion of an aircraft; and therefore a tilting forward or backward (from the vertical) of the spacecraft. The pitch axis is a horizontal line running left-to-right (perpendicular to the orbit plane) through the spacecraft. Roll in an aircraft is a rotation around the long axis, or a wing-up or -down attitude. For spacecraft, it is a tilt to left or right. The roll axis is a horizontal line from front to back. Yaw is a rotation to the left or right about the vertical (or yaw) axis.

Vertical orientation will be considered first. The horizon scanners, Figure 10-5, have a narrow field of view, at 45° to the roll axis, and rapidly rotate around the roll axis to form a cone of view. The scanners distinguish earth from space by temperature differences, the same as the TIROS horizon scanners (Chapter 5). When the spacecraft is vertical, the scanner axis references (marked "Spacecraft Local Vertical" in Figure 10-5) are half-way between the horizons in both scanners. Furthermore, both scanners see the same amount of earth (i.e., the same fraction of a total scanner revolution is between the horizons).

Assume the axis is not vertical, but tilted forward (in pitch)

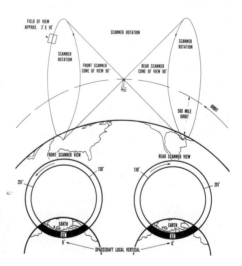

Fig. 10-5. Earth as seen by horizon scanners in the Nimbus when stabilized. (NASA)

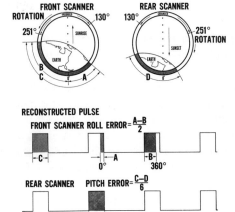

FRONT SCANNER
ROTATION 130° 130°
251° SUNRISE 251° ROTATION
EARTH SUNSET
B EARTH
C A D C̄

RECONSTRUCTED PULSE
FRONT SCANNER ROLL ERROR=$\frac{A-B}{2}$

|←C→| |←A| |←B→|
0° 360°

REAR SCANNER PITCH ERROR=$\frac{C-D}{6}$

|←D→|

Fig. 10-6. Roll and pitch error detection by the front and rear Nimbus horizon scanners. (NASA)

and to the left in roll (Figure 10-6). Due to the pitch error, the front scanner sees more earth than the rear. This difference is detected as an error by the Controls Computer, and its direction and amount are calculated.

The computer operates flywheels and gas jets (pneumatics) to correct these errors in orientation (Figure 10-7). Flywheels correct small errors (less than ± 3°) and gas jets larger ones. As an example, consider the roll error; the operation in pitch is entirely analogous. Since the spacecraft is tilted to the left, it needs to rotate to the right or clockwise. From the principle of the Conservation of Angular Momentum, if a flywheel with its axis parallel to the roll axis accelerates counterclockwise, the spacecraft will turn clockwise. The principle is the same as the tendency of a small power drill to turn in your hand when you turn it on; in attempting to maintain constant angular momentum, the drill case and handle try to turn opposite to the rotation of the motor rotor. The small flywheel must turn rapidly to produce even a slow rotation of the comparatively massive spacecraft. This aids in precise control of the spacecraft attitude. Slow rotations of the spacecraft are desirable since they prevent blurring of pictures.

Based on the horizon scanner signals, the computer controls the flywheel motor direction and speed, in this case causing it to rotate counterclockwise. As the spacecraft approaches the vertical (zero roll), the computer adjusts the motor to stop the spacecraft rotation in the vertical position (to within $\pm 1°$).

If the roll error exceeds three degrees, the computer opens a valve to eject a small amount of nitrogen gas from the proper nozzle. The nozzles are mounted on the top of the turret (Figure 10-3). To rotate the spacecraft clockwise, the gas must be ejected from the left nozzle.

The gas ejection system has two other functions. It is used to orient Nimbus after launch. Furthermore, there is a maximum safe rate of flywheel rotation. When this rate is neared, gas ejected from the proper nozzle compensates for a simultaneous slowing of the motor speed. This is known as flywheel desaturation or "dumping." It is analogous to the use of a generator in a car to keep the battery recharged.

Nimbus carries enough nitrogen gas for at least a six-month stabilized life in orbit including (1) initial orientation; (2) a second reorientation if ever needed; (3) normal maintenance of stabilization; and (4) the necessary desaturations of the

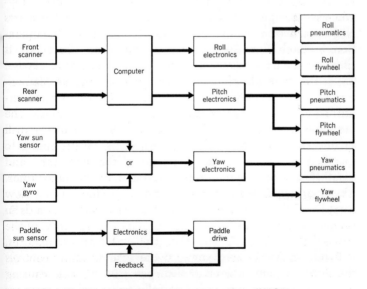

Fig. 10-7. Nimbus control subsystem operation. (NASA)

flywheels. The Nimbus I controls subsystem worked very well, attitude errors seldom exceeded $3°$, and so only a minimal use of gas was required.

Pitch errors, detected by comparing the indications of the two horizon sensors, are corrected by similar use of a flywheel whose axis is parallel to the pitch axis, and front and rear pointing gas nozzles. To maintain verticality as the satellite rotates around the earth, the satellite must rotate in pitch once per orbit (about each 108 minutes). Once this motion, sometimes referred to as a "controlled tumble," is established, however, it maintains itself by Conservation of Angular Momentum with only slight control system adjustments required. The pitch flywheels also compensate for rotations of the solar paddles, which keep the solar cells facing the sun.

One of the principal problems during the development of the Nimbus control system was the horizon sensors which are the only source of vertical reference and control. Originally, it was planned to use the 8-12 micron window, the infrared region used for the TIROS horizon sensors. The effects of clouds, which made it difficult to determine TIROS orientation (see Chapter 5), were too great a complication for the Nimbus Controls computer; it was not able to tell a horizon from a cloud edge. A carbon dioxide emission band centered about 15 microns wavelength was substituted. In this region, the atmosphere absorbs so strongly that only occasionally is a cloud seen (mainly very high tropical thunderstorms). Unfortunately the energy emitted in this region is less and the infrared detectors are also less sensitive. Because of this, the accuracy of stabilization was slightly less than originally specified. To provide information to aid the development of these 15 micron horizon scanners, a sensor operating in this region was included in the TIROS VII scanning radiometer; it replaced the 6.3 micron water vapor band sensor (see Reference 6-4).

Besides keeping Nimbus vertical, it was necessary to keep it facing forward (zero yaw) so the solar paddles face the sun and the cameras and radiometers have proper fields of view. The correct position is originally sensed by a sun sensor and maintained by a gyro. Each sun sensor (Figure 10-3) consists of several solar cells mounted about a vertical half-cylinder. If there is a yaw error, more power is generated by the solar cells on one side than the other. These signals, processed by the Controls computer, operate a flywheel (whose axis is parallel to the yaw or vertical axis), or yaw gas nozzles mounted on the sides of the turret; the satellite is rotated about the yaw axis to the correct orientation, using the same principle as for roll orientation. Because the sun cannot be seen on the night side of the earth, a gyro, engaged after initial orientation using the sun, thereafter controls yaw. If the gyro drifts excessively, ground command reinstitutes sun sensor control until the gyro is reoriented.

If the gyro develops a bias, creating a steady yaw error, or if the orbit drifts from its desired orientation, ground commands can set in yaw bias corrections.

The controls system also rotates the solar paddles so they always face the sun on the daylight side of the earth. Solar array sun sensors are mounted on the paddle shafts (Figure 10-3). The illumination on these cells (if not uniform relative to the plane of the paddles) generates electrical currents which control a motor and drive the paddles to the correct position. Because of the slow pitch rotation, to maintain spacecraft verticality, the paddles should rotate continually on the sunlit side of the earth. When the satellite enters the earth's shadow, the motor drives the paddles to the position where, when they again re-enter sunlight, they will generate maximum power.

The paddle shaft was the Achille's heel of Nimbus I. About four weeks after launch, the shaft began to rotate erratically and soon ceased to turn at all. The spacecraft died from the resulting loss of power. It would appear that some bearing failed, either in the shaft drive mechanism or where the shaft enters the control turret. Adequate lubrication and sealing of bearings exposed to the vacuum of space is, at best, a difficult problem. The launch of the next Nimbus will be delayed until improved procedures can be incorporated.

Spacecraft attitude must be known as accurately as possible

for geographically locating the cloud pictures and radiation data. Readings of the horizon sensors, sun sensors, gyros, etc. (and other information on the performance of the controls subsystem) are recorded by the Engineering (PCM) Telemetry subsystem and radioed to the ground upon command.

During development, the Controls subsystem was tested on an air-bearing suspension, mounted in front of a disk to simulate the earth for the horizon sensors. This disk moves around the suspended controls system and almost all of the control functions are tested. The Nimbus Control and Stabilization subsystem was the first three-axis satellite control system to undergo full three-dimensional ground functional testing prior to flight.

The Controls subsystem worked very well on Nimbus I. Gas valving was seldom needed. Because of brief but excessive horizon sensor responses to occasional high, cold clouds and an undue sensitivity of the gas valve controls to the resulting rotational accelerations of the spacecraft, attitude was best maintained by commanding the gas valves to remain inactive most of the time. The flywheels alone maintained accurate attitude control, with only a brief and infrequent gas valving for wheel desaturation. Prior to the failure of the paddle shaft bearings, it appeared the nitrogen gas supply would be so slowly drained that a full year's useful life in orbit was entirely possible.

Power Subsystem

The Nimbus power subsystem is an improved version of the TIROS subsystem. It provides about ten times the power with greater electrical reliability. The major differences are:

(1) Mounting the solar cells on paddles, which are turned to face directly towards the sun, thus maximizing power.

(2) The use of solar cells electrically the reverse of those used on TIROS to minimize the effects of the artificial radiation belt produced by the 1962 Starfish atomic test.

The solar paddles (sometimes called platforms or arrays), mounted on shafts that protrude from the Controls turret, are hinged for folding into launching position and deployment to operating position after injection into orbit. Each paddle is about 3 by 8 feet in size. It consists of two sheets of thin aluminum, connected together for maximum strength (to withstand the vibrations of launch) by an aluminum honeycomb core. The solar cells are mounted on the face; the reverse is a coating chosen to maximize heat radiation to space, which keeps the cells cool and efficient.

Each of the 10,500 cells is 2 × 2 cm in size (twice the size of those in TIROS). Although their number is only about 10 per cent greater than the 9,260 cells TIROS carries, the Nimbus cells provide about ten times as much power since they are twice as large and all face the sun. This is another bonus from earth stabilization.

When Nimbus was designed, it was hoped that the solar cells would provide 450 watts of power when in sunlight. An actual power of about 400 watts was achieved. Since ⅓ of each orbit is spent in darkness, an average of 250 watts is available.

The power generated by the cells is fed along the shaft, through slip rings, and to the over 140 nickel-cadmium storage batteries and the regulators housed in the sensory ring. Controls prevent excessive charging rates and overvoltages, share loads, and regulate voltages. The system provides regulated power at 24.5 volts D.C. to an accuracy of ± 2 per cent. The other spacecraft equipments are designed for this power. The subsystem was designed and built by RCA Astro-Electronics Division.

Command-Clock Subsystem

The Nimbus Command-Clock combines three functions in a single unit at a saving of weight, power and space. These functions are:

(1) To serve as a clock and furnish the time whenever needed. Nimbus differs from TIROS in that commands are executed at specified times rather than after a length of time has elapsed. Nimbus executes a given command at say, 1030

hours (10:30 AM) whereas a TIROS command is executed after a period of say, 35 minutes. The time and place of command execution can be precise without high precision in the time of sending the command. The difference is like that between an automatic kitchen oven control which can turn the oven on at a specified time, compared to the minute-timer which runs a set length of time after being started.

(2) To furnish a variety of precise and stable frequencies, ranging from 1 cycle per second to 400 kilocycles per second, to control the functions of various equipments.

(3) To accept commands from the ground, verify them, reject spurious radio signals, store legitimate commands, and execute them at the proper time.

Because future execution requires both timing and command storage, it was convenient to combine the Command and the Clock functions.

The Command or receiving antenna is a rod, mounted on a cone-like array on the controls turret (Figure 10-2). This cone and other rods around the trusses aid proper reception of commands even if the satellite has lost stabilization. Command signals are sent at a VHF (Very High Frequency) wavelength.

The signals go to one of two receivers, which are in redundancy to protect against the failures. These receivers amplify and demodulate the command signal and pass it to the command-clock.

The command portion of the subsystem first checks the signal. If it is found to be legitimate, the subsystem stores it for execution at the time specified, which may be as soon as three seconds later. Commands can be received and executed at the rate of one per second. Five can be in storage (for periods up to 24 hours) at any one time. As many as 30 commands can easily be accepted during one pass over a Command and Data Acquisition (CDA) station. There can be 128 different commands.

In general, the commands are limited to switching on or off various equipments, or to switching in redundant units. Adjustments are limited to a very few critical functions.

If the primary command system should fail, a few unencoded commands, of types vital to minimum spacecraft operation and obtaining information on the causes of failures, can be sent and accepted.

The heart of the clock is a stable crystal with a frequency of exactly 800 kilocycles per second. The crystal is sealed and maintained at a constant temperature of 60°C. The crystal and its associated oscillator are accurate to one part in 10^7 (10,000,000); that is, the clock would be in error by no more than one second at the end of 115 days. Even so, the clock can be reset, after the satellite is in orbit, to insure maximum accuracy.

The 800-Kc rate is successively divided and redivided by factors of 2, 4, and 5, using electronic devices known as multivibrators, to provide the lower frequencies needed by the various equipments. The uses of a few of these frequencies are discussed below:

The television cameras operate on 400 cps (cycles per second) current, just as most home appliances are designed for 60-cycle current. The TV tape recorders run at an exact rate established by the 400 cps frequency current. A 1 cps signal times the interval between AVCS pictures. A 50-Kc signal is recorded and measured on the ground to control picture playback and to minimize distortion.

The 50-Kc and 10-Kc frequencies are modulated to transmit time information. The time code pulses have a rate of 100 cps, and their lengths are established by a 500-cps frequency.

The 500-cps frequency also controls the pulses that transmit engineering telemetry. A 10 cps frequency provides an emergency engineering telemetry unit.

The time registered on the clock is sent once each second over the tracking beacons, except during periods when they are transmitting engineering telemetry data. From this, time errors in the clock setting (even if very small) become known on the ground.

The command-clock (except the antenna and receiver), including its housing, is built into a 6" × 8" × 13" module, weighing only 18 pounds and using only 9 watts of power. The subsystem (except for the RCA receiver) was designed and built by California Computer Products.

Engineering Telemetry Subsystem

Engineering Telemetry provides information on the operation and status of the many Nimbus equipments; in the case of failure, the subsystem permits diagnosis of the causes and perhaps leads to ways to partially overcome them. By this point, as Dr. Stampfl has so well stated (see Reference 10-G-1): "The complexity of the spacecraft should be well appreciated, making a justification for analytical telemetry superfluous. Engineering evaluation of the system in orbit will provide a basis for more reliable designs in the future. This evaluation will also permit the life of the spacecraft to be prolonged since malfunctioning subsystems can be turned off through the command system or can be replaced by redundant modules."

In addition to this function, the telemetry subsystem provides data from the Controls on spacecraft orientation for use in locating the pictures and other data. The subsystem can also be used to store and transmit information from low data rate sensors. Such an experiment might be a solar constant sensor, since variations in total solar radiation are not rapid.

The Nimbus telemetry system provides information on temperatures, pressures, voltages, settings, etc., from the several Nimbus subsystems. For example, in monitoring the controls subsystem it provides:

    (1) Temperatures of the exterior panels of the turret;
    (2) Positions of the temperature control shutters;
    (3) Temperature and pressure of the nitrogen gas;
    (4) Gyro temperatures and regulating signals;
    (5) Horizon scanner temperatures and signals;
    (6) Sun sensor signals;
    (7) Flywheel temperatures, speeds, and directions;
    (8) Gas valve operation and settings;
    (9) Electrical signals in and from the subsystem computer.

Some 50 points are monitored and recorded from this subsystem alone.

TIROS makes engineering telemetry measurements only when near a command and data acquisition station—no storage is provided. In Nimbus, the data are recorded, using an improved continuous loop tape recorder similar to that used on TIROS for radiometric data. The capacity of the tape (240 feet recorded at 0.4 inches per second) permits recording slightly more than one orbit of data. If not then readout, the oldest data are progressively erased as newer data are recorded, leaving data from the last orbit always available.

The telemetry system can record 64 different values per second. Many points do not need to be recorded so frequently. By subcommutation (switching) 542 points can be monitored, 31 once a second and others once per sixteen seconds. In later Nimbus satellites, 798 points can be sampled, using additional subcommutations.

Some data points are critical and are monitored through different channels to insure obtaining their data. Accordingly, less than 542 separate points are monitored. In the event of a recorder failure, the system can directly radio the data being sampled.

Ground command causes tape recorder playback at 30 times the recording speed. All data recorded during an orbit can be played-out in under 4 minutes.

The telemetry system which records the data is called the "A" system (sometimes "PCM-A"). Because of the importance of insuring engineering data, a separate and simpler "B" system is also provided. It samples only the most critical 128 points. Like the TIROS system it has no storage and can provide only measurements within range of a data acquisition station.

Like all advanced Goddard Space Flight Center spacecraft, the engineering telemetry subsystem uses Pulse Code Modulation (PCM); it transmits only two types of signals. It is a system where one signal stands for "zero" and the other for "one."

The telemetry subsystem (or PCM subsystem, as it is often

referred to) data are transmitted through 350-milliwatt beacon transmitters, which are provided in redundancy. Each uses a separate frequency near 136 megacycles. During most of an orbit the beacon transmits time, as read from the clock. On command, transmission of the PCM data is initiated. Upon completion of the PCM readouts, beacon transmission for position tracking and orbit computation is resumed.

Transmitting antennas, of a type known as a quadraloop, are mounted equally spaced around the sides of the sensory ring. Four are used to insure reception of the telemetry data, even if the controls system fails and the satellite is tumbling.

Although Nimbus was designed for meteorological observations, this basic spacecraft is adaptable to other objectives (for example, it has been considered for oceanographic observations). However, only sensors developed for meteorological observations will be discussed in this book.

The Advanced Vidicon Camera Subsystem (AVCS)

Nimbus carries two camera systems for observing clouds and the other features seen by the TIROS cameras. One system, the AVCS cameras, provides global data for use in the National Meteorological Center and transmission (usually as nephanalyses) by regular weather communications to weather stations through the world. The second, the Automatic Picture Transmission (APT) subsystem, provides pictures of local cloud patterns directly to suitably equipped weather stations as the satellite passes near them.

The AVCS subsystem is discussed here; the APT subsystem in the following section.

The Advanced Vidicon Camera Subsystem consists of three cameras, mounted in a tri-metragon array similar to that used for aerial photography. The center camera points straight down while each side camera is directed at a 35° angle. The field of view of each camera is 37° of angle along a side, as seen from the lens. The total field of view of the set (from side to side) covers 107°. This provides a slight overlap in coverage from one orbit to the next, even at the equator, for orbit altitudes of about 500 nautical miles or greater. Near the poles, there is considerable overlap between adjacent orbits. A slight overlap between the fields of view of the central and side cameras assists in matching the pictures from the three cameras.

There is one weakness in this arrangement which would be serious if there should ever be significant errors in maintaining the vertical orientation of the satellite. The coverage of the cameras does not include the horizons. This is because the oblique view and poor resolution near the horizon provide limited meteorological data, and the areas near the horizon are normally viewed at a favorable angle on an adjacent orbit. Omitting the horizon region permits better resolution. On the other side of the coin, however, horizons are extremely valuable in establishing TIROS attitude and, in the event of a partial failure of the Nimbus controls, could perform a similar service.

Nimbus AVCS pictures are taken as a triplet (one from each camera) once every 91 seconds over the daylight portion of the orbit. A slight overlap along the orbit is provided from one triplet to the next. Thirty-two triplets (96 pictures from the three cameras) provide complete coverage along the orbit from "satellite-rise" (relative to the sun) near the south pole, to "satellite-set" near the north pole. The solar paddles shaft rotation (which keeps the paddles facing the sun) operates a switch that starts the cameras near the south pole and turns them off (32 triplets later) near the north pole.

Figure 10-8 shows a set of AVCS cameras assembled on their mounting brackets. They operate basically the same as the TIROS cameras. Certain significant differences, however, provide the greatly improved performance of the AVCS subsystem. The vidicon is a one-inch tube compared to the one-half inch ones in TIROS, and it is scanned with an 800-line raster while TIROS uses only 500 lines. This and the reduced angle of view for each camera ($37°$ compared to $84°$ for TIROS) provides a one-half mile ground resolution per TV line, whereas TIROS gives a two-to-three mile resolution.

Fig. 10-8. Nimbus AVCS cameras. (NASA)

Much more detail is to be seen in the cloud pictures on a
world-wide basis (although not as much as in the small areas
photographed by the narrow angle camera used on TIROS I
and II). Note, for example, the sand spit at the ocean edge
of the Sabkhet el Bardawil lagoon in the upper right of
Figure 1-5a (east of the mouth of the Suez Canal). This feature was never really visible in even the best of the TIROS
pictures of Egypt.

Because Nimbus does not rotate, a 40-millisecond exposure
is used. This permits pictures near the poles, not normally
possible on TIROS, even if the orbit permitted, due to low
sun angle and poor illumination.

To make maximum use of this additional exposure while
preventing overexposure near the brighter equator, the cameras have a variable iris—lens opening. Iris positions are controlled by the rotation of the solar paddle shaft. The iris
position varies from wide open near the south pole (paddles
parallel to the vertical and facing forward) to minimum opening at the equator (paddles horizontal) to wide open again
near the north pole (paddles again parallel to the vertical but
facing backward). The gears that vary the iris are on the
front of each camera (Figure 10-8). For redundancy, two iris

motors are provided on each camera, either of which is sufficient. As further protection against total failure, if some
portion of the iris control malfunctions, a fixed intermediate
setting can be ordered from the ground.

For accurate location of the clouds, good reference marks are
needed. In TIROS, only relatively rough marks (the central +
and corner "L" marks in the TIROS pictures) are scribed onto
the vidicon surface. They are indispensable, but leave much
to be desired. In Nimbus, a precise pattern of 25 fiducial
marks is provided (see Figure 1-5a).

In TIROS there is no way to determine the exact brightness
of the clouds photographed. In Nimbus, a brightness scale is
included along one edge of each picture. A constant intensity
flash lamp illuminates a "grey-wedge" while each exposure
is being made. This provides a brightness comparison strip,
on the picture, which ranges from very dark to very bright. In
using this calibration to determine the brightness of clouds,
the setting of the variable iris must also be considered.

As in TIROS, the picture is snapped and then slowly
scanned off; in Nimbus, the scan takes 6.5 seconds. As the data
are scanned off, they are tape recorded. Between pictures, as
in TIROS, the tape recorder stops.

The Nimbus AVCS tape recorder is an improved version
of that used for the TIROS cloud pictures. The data from all
three cameras are recorded in parallel on separate tracks. A
fourth track carries timing pulses to identify when the pictures
are taken and a 50-kilocycle tone used to minimize distortion
when they are reproduced.

All AVCS pictures are stored in the recorder (which holds
two orbits' data) until readout is commanded. The recorder
then plays back continuously, with no stops between pictures.
Since playback is at the same speed as the recording (30
inches per second), 32 triplets are played back in 208 seconds.

The pictures from the three cameras, the timing channel,
and four channels of High Resolution Infrared Radiometer
(HRIR) data and timing signals (described later), are simultaneously transmitted to the ground by a single S-band (1700
megacycle) five-watt transmitter, operating over a 700 Kc

bandwidth. The eight concurrent AVCS and HRIR data channels are kept separate by frequency multiplexing, just as for the several channels of TIROS radiometer data. Local oscillators add or subtract frequencies to each channel.

The AVCS-HRIR antenna is mounted on the base of the spacecraft (useful pictures can be taken only if the satellite is properly oriented). It is a specially designed fiberglass cone with copper spirals printed on its surface.

The Nimbus AVCS system and tape recorder were designed and developed by RCA's Astro-Electronics Division. The S-band transmitter is by General Electronics Laboratory. The antenna was designed at the University of New Mexico.

During less than one month of useful operation, Nimbus I took about 12,000 AVCS pictures. Figure 10-9 is a series of Nimbus AVCS triplets, taken over North Africa and Western Europe on August 30, 1964. The peninsulas of Brittany and Cherbourg, in France, are only two of the landmarks that are clearly visible.

The Automatic Picture Transmission (APT) Subsystem

There are high correlations between the size of a meteorological feature (such as a cloud or storm), its lifetime, and the distance and time over which it is of significance. Large systems, such as extratropical cyclones, last for days and influence the weather over large areas; very small systems (such as individual thunderstorms) last only an hour or so, and affect the weather only over a small area.

These relationships create a serious problem when designing meteorological satellite systems. The details in the cloud patterns, as seen by TIROS or the Nimbus AVCS cameras, are available almost only at central points such as the CDA stations, the National Meteorological Center, and a few major weather centrals. They are not available at the local weather stations, in the immediate vicinity of each of these smaller features, where the data would be of greatest use. Limitations to weather communications prevent distribution of data details, and permit wide dissemination only of far grosser analyses. Even if such distribution were possible, considerable time would elapse while the satellite orbits from the point of photography to the point of read-out, and while the picture is processed and sent back to weather stations in the area photographed. This time would be more than sufficient for small features to dissipate.

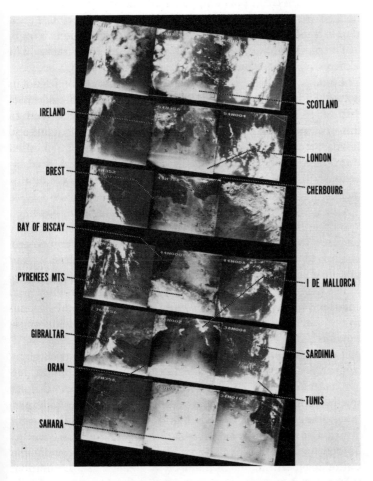

Fig. 10-9.   A series of AVCS pictures across Western Europe. (NASA)

The Nimbus Automatic Picture Transmission (APT) Subsystem overcomes this problem. Instead of storing the picture for readout at a CDA station, the APT subsystem transmits it immediately for reception and use at properly equipped local weather stations within line of sight (a radius of about 1000 miles) of the satellite. The equipment required at the stations is comparatively inexpensive, costing only a few tens of thousands of dollars as compared to the few million dollars needed for a TIROS or Nimbus CDA station. The APT system is a most significant development in satellite meteorology.

The heart of the APT subsystem is a specially developed vidicon tube, the same in most respects as the AVCS vidicon. The major differences are two additional layers not found in normal vidicon tubes. After the image is recorded, as a pattern of electrons on the normal surfaces, it is transferred to the new surfaces where it can be stored almost indefinitely. Read-off scanning can take place at a slow rate. This permits transmission over a narrow bandwidth, less than that used by ordinary telephones, and reception by relatively simple equipment.

The special storage layer, vital to the APT system, has been a source of major problems. Erasing the surface, between pictures, gradually degrades the quality of the pictures and severely limits the useful life of the system. After a few thousand pictures, contrast is inadequate.

The APT camera provides a picture slightly greater than one-thousand miles on a side with a resolution midway between that of the Nimbus AVCS and the TIROS wide angle cameras. This is illustrated in Figure 10-10, a Nimbus I APT picture of the northeastern United States. Compare it with the frontispiece, taken by TIROS VII.

A station in mid-latitudes, equipped to receive APT data, can receive about three pictures from a pass essentially over the station, and one or two pictures from directly adjacent orbits. Four to seven pictures of the surrounding area should be received within two hours of noon each day, with the station itself within one of them.

Picture taking and transmission is begun at daylight of each

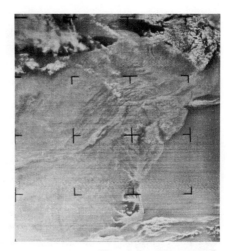

Fig. 10-10. A Nimbus I
APT picture of the north-
eastern United States.
(NASA)

orbit. The sequence repeats automatically each 208 seconds
until darkness again turns off the system. No ground commands from the local weather stations are needed or possible.
The Nimbus CDA stations can program turn-off of the system, either temporarily or permanently.

The sequence in the satellite is as follows (see Reference
10-G-5): The vidicon surface is erased and prepared to receive a new picture. When the shutter is triggered, the image
is projected on the vidicon surface, after which it is electronically "developed," i.e., transferred to the storage layer.
These operations occur during the first eight seconds of each
sequence. During the remaining 200 seconds, the picture is
scanned at four lines per second.

The scanning uses a sampling technique to reduce noise.
The signals have a 2400-cps bandwidth. The five-watt transmitter operates in the 136-megacycle band. The single quadraloop antenna is mounted on the bottom of the ring.

APT receiving equipment is shown in Figure 10-11. The
antenna is controlled at a console, and does not auto-track;
this would greatly increase the cost. A low set cost is desirable to make it feasible for many weather stations to have
such sets, especially in countries where funds for weather
services are limited.

Fig. 10-11.   The APT ground receiving antenna. (NASA)

Satellite tracking is aided by a 40° antenna receiving angle, compared to a very few degrees for a large CDA antenna. Precise tracking is not required. Antenna directions are calculated from teletyped orbit information, using a tracking board and procedure developed by ARACON Geophysics Company (see Reference 10-4).

Maps and methods for locating APT pictures have also been developed by ARACON Geophysics Company. They are simplifications of the overlay techniques developed for TIROS I; earth orientation of the satellite reduces the location problem.

The APT system should be widely used in weather stations both in the United States and overseas, particularly in areas where other weather data are insufficient. It may be widely used on television weather programs; the APT cloud pictures would vividly display to the TV audience the weather conditions in the area; assuming, of course, proper interpretation by the broadcaster. With these various applications in mind, there is considerable interest in reducing the cost of the ground stations from their initial value of slightly over $30,000.

In due course, a commercial kit for amateur construction of private APT sets may become available. A non-scanning, wide-beam antenna might be used, with a time-exposure Polaroid camera recording from a TV screen. The major problem involved in converting an ordinary TV set to this use would be attaining the very slow scan required to match the satellite camera.

Due to the delays in launching Nimbus I, TIROS VIII was modified to test fly an APT camera. Although intended primarily as an engineering test and a chance to check-out the ground stations, some operational use was made of the data. The results were moderately successful, with most of the problems arising from the spin of TIROS.

High Resolution Infrared Radiometer (HRIR)

The Nimbus AVCS and APT cameras provide cloud observations during daylight, half of each orbit. An analogous night capability is needed, so that conditions can be observed once every twelve hours. It is provided by the High Resolution Infrared Radiometer (HRIR).

The HRIR operates on the principle described in Chapter 6. Its infrared response is limited to an atmospheric "window" where radiation comes from the earth's surface in clear areas, and from cloud tops. Since cloud tops are normally colder than the surface, they emit less energy and register colder. Thus the radiometer can provide a map of cloudy and clear areas, and some estimate of the heights of the cloud tops.

In TIROS the 8-12 micron window channel was used. Although earth and atmospheric infrared radiation is a maximum at these wavelengths (in accordance with their temperatures and Planck's Laws), ten-micron detectors are far less sensitive than those for shorter wavelengths. Because of these detector limitations, the Nimbus HRIR operates in another atmospheric window, between 3.4 and 4.2 microns, where better sensitivity and resolution are possible.

Near four microns, there is, during daylight, reflected solar

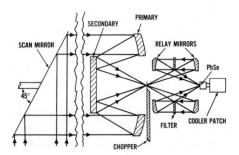

Fig. 10-12. Schematic of the Nimbus HRIR. (NASA)

radiation as well as emitted infrared radiation. Because of this, the HRIR data are most useful at night; during daytime, the combination of emitted and reflected radiation is often difficult to interpret. With AVCS pictures available, the greater resolution possible near four microns makes this limitation acceptable. The only daytime loss is the cloud top altitude data and, in later Nimbus, this information will be available from the Medium Resolution Infrared Radiometer (MRIR) to be described in the next section. Accordingly, HRIR electronics are normally shut-off during daytime, by a switch on the solar paddles shaft. If desired, an override command can keep the system operating during the day. The scanning motor is kept running to minimize bearing problems.

Originally it was hoped to attain about a one-and-a-half mile HRIR resolution. This was not possible and the Nimbus I resolution was expected to be five miles. A somewhat better resolution actually resulted but only due to the low night-time altitude of the eccentric Nimbus I orbit.

The HRIR operation is best described using the schematic in Figure 10-12. A rotating mirror provides a horizon-to-horizon scan perpendicular to the direction of motion of the satellite; the spacecraft motion causes the scanned line to move forward along the orbit. The radiometer is mounted on the base of Nimbus with the mirror shaft parallel to the roll axis. The mirror is mounted at a 45° angle, as can be seen in Figure 10-12. The rotation of the mirror causes the field of view of the detector to scan from space across the horizon, across the earth, back out to space, across the radiometer housing just below the satellite's base, and back to space again. The mirror rotates at 44.7 rpm; the satellite advances the width of one scan line during each scan. This provides complete coverage with little overlap at the subpoint; toward the horizon increasing overlap is tolerated, since it is preferable to areas of underlap (no coverage).

The near $0°K$ temperature during views of space provides one calibration point. A second calibration, at a temperature near that of the earth's surface, is provided by a "black-body," with measured and telemetered temperature, mounted in the radiometer housing and scanned when the field of view is straight up. These two calibration points are superior to the single space temperature reference of the TIROS scanning radiometer; they permit the calibration scale to be expanded or contracted, as well as just displaced, in accordance with the readings observed.

A magnet on the mirror axis triggers electronic equipment and synchronizes ground playback to scanning in the satellite.

The radiation is focused on the lead selenide (PbSe) detector by an array of mirrors. The filter between the mirrors limits the radiation to wavelengths between 3.4 and 4.2 microns. The chopper, which intermittently cuts the radiation, allows amplification of an alternating current (AC) signal. This avoids many problems of amplifier bias, since a difference rather than an absolute value is measured. (This is analogous to a watch which, although set wrong, can still measure lengths of time).

A lead selenide (PbSe) detector is far more sensitive at low temperatures than at the room temperatures normal in a satellite with a good thermal design. (Most other satellite equipment works best near room temperatures.) The HRIR detector is cooled to about $-74°C$ (about $-101°F$) by radiation to space. Thermally connected to the detector is a pyramid made of a good heat conductor. The detector is at the apex of the pyramid; the base, coated black (to maximize radiation cooling), looks to the side where it always sees only cold black space.

A cooled detector is more sensitive because of the random

molecular, atomic, and electronic motions becoming slower and
fewer as the temperature is reduced. Such motions (especially
those of electrons) produce electronic noise (static)—since an
electrical signal is electrons moving through a wire or a space.
The fewer such random motions, the less the noise and the
better the desired signal can be amplified and measured.

The detector signal is amplified and stored in a modified
AVCS tape recorder. On the first orbit, two of the four tracks
are used, one for the signal and the other for 10-Kc timing
pulses. If a second orbit is recorded, the recorder reverses
and the other two tracks are used. All four tracks are read
out, simultaneously with the AVCS data using frequency
multiplexing and the AVCS S-band transmitter as discussed
for that subsystem.

Nimbus I acquired about 6200 minutes of HRIR data. This
is equal to more than 90 strips from the north to the south
pole. A small portion of one strip (Figure 10-13) showed
Hurricane Dora over northern Florida, and the middle Atlantic coast of the United States. The data are reproduced
with cold areas (clouds) white, and warm areas dark. The
temperature sensitivity of HRIR is demonstrated by the clearly
visible coast, the warm ocean water temperatures (black)
contrasting with the cooler nighttime land (grey). (When

Fig. 10-13. A Nimbus
I HRIR picture of Hur-
ricane Dora. (NASA)

looking at HRIR pictures, it is vital to remember a *temperature contrast*, not a contrast in reflectivity, creates the picture.)
The excellent resolution is shown by Dora's eye, and the
distinct shapes of Chesapeake and Delaware Bays; compare
this HRIR picture with those of this area by TIROS (the
Frontispiece) and the Nimbus APT (Figure 10-10).

Medium Resolution Infrared Radiometer (MRIR)

The Medium Resolution Infrared Radiometer scans the
earth and atmosphere using the same type of rotating mirror
as in the HRIR. The radiation is reflected onto five separate
detectors which measure basically the same radiation bands
as the TIROS five-channel radiometer.

As for the TIROS scanning radiometer, the resolution of
MRIR is about 30 miles when looking straight down. Several
MRIR filters are improvements of those in TIROS. In the
"window" channel, the bandpass has been reduced from 8-12
microns (in TIROS) to 10-11 microns in MRIR. This leads to
a much clearer "window" by eliminating detrimental atmospheric absorption.

For the infrared channels, a reference in the housing provides calibration data. The sun is used as a second calibration
point for the solar-radiation channels (see Reference 10-G-5).

The MRIR data are frequency multiplexed for simultaneous recording; the recorder is basically the same as that
used for PCM telemetry. Transmission to the ground is by
an FM transmitter in the 136 Mc band, and a quadraloop
antenna on the base of the sensory ring.

Because of weight limitations imposed by the launch vehicle,
MRIR was not carried on Nimbus I. Both MRIR and HRIR
are expected to be included in later Nimbus satellites.

Qualification Testing

Nimbus qualification testing was similar to that of TIROS
(see Reference 10-G-5).

In addition to separate humidity, vibration, acceleration and thermal vacuum testing of each subsystem, the sensory ring was tested separately prior to attachment of the trusses and the previously tested controls subsystem. Then the entire spacecraft was fully tested and qualified. All subsystems, the sensory ring, and the complete spacecraft underwent both prototype and flight model qualifications.

Thermal vacuum testing of the spacecraft took place in the 39-foot diameter chamber at General Electric's Missile and Space Division (Figure 10-14). During this testing, the spacecraft was mounted on an air-bearing. Three-dimensional operation of the controls system under thermal vacuum conditions was demonstrated.

During the thermal vacuum test, it is necessary to "hook-up" to the spacecraft to recharge the batteries, because of the absence of solar power, and to bring targets within the view of the detectors to check their calibration. This was done by a check of calibration adapter (with targets mounted on it) and a ram which pushed it in or out of the vacuum chamber using an air-lock to prevent loss of vacuum. The development of the supporting equipments for the Nimbus testing was a major project in itself.

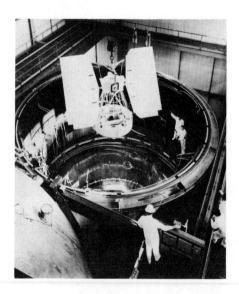

Fig. 10-14. Thirty-nine-foot vacuum-thermal chamber used for Nimbus testing. (NASA, GE)

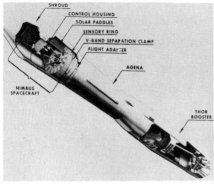

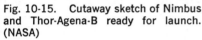

Fig. 10-15. Cutaway sketch of Nimbus and Thor-Agena-B ready for launch. (NASA)

Fig. 10-16. The Nimbus I launch from PMR. (NASA)

Launch Vehicle and Launch Procedure

Nimbus I was placed in orbit by a Thor-Agena. An artist's "cut-away" of Nimbus ready for launch, with paddles folded and shroud attached, is shown in Figure 10-15.

The Thor-Agena has a restriction on its attainable payload weight and orbit altitude. As the weight of Nimbus I exceeded original estimates, even with some subsystems and considerable redundancy dropped, and due also to decreases in expected Thor-Agena capabilities, the planned Nimbus orbit altitude was progressively reduced.

In later Nimbus, it is hoped to exceed the originally planned orbit altitude and subsystem redundancies, and to add additional subsystems, by using a more powerful launch vehicle. The more likely approach is the Thrust-Augmented Thor. In this configuration, the Thor is given greater thrust by adding three externally-mounted solid rockets.

Nimbus I was launched (Figure 10-16) from the Pacific Missile Range on August 28, 1964. This is presently the only launch site with a Thor Agena pad and a clear overwater trajectory for U. S. polar orbit launches. The launch is at about an 80° inclination, 10° to the west of due south, usually referred to as an 80° retrograde orbit, because the east-west part of the velocity is opposite to the direction of the earth's rotation and requires additional thrust. At this inclination and an altitude of about 500-700 nautical miles, the angle between the orbit plane and the sun remains fixed (see Chapter 12 or Reference 10-6). By launching near midnight (or noon) the equator crossings of the satellite orbit are always near local noon and midnight; this insures maximum illumination for the solar cells and the cameras. By launching near midnight, the northbound equator crossing was at noon and the detailed cloud pictures could be read-out by the Fairbanks, Alaska, CDA station with minimum delay.

Pre-launch check-out and testing were analogous to that for TIROS, but, of course, far more complex. All Nimbus check-outs were by radio; for this reason, a radio-frequency-transparent shroud was used.

The launch and injection sequence is shown in Figure 10-17. After Thor burn-out, the shroud nosecone is ejected, the Agena and the attached Nimbus separate from the Thor, and Agena first burn is initiated. The second stage-spacecraft combination then have sufficient velocity to coast to orbit altitude. This, known as a transfer ellipse, takes place over a distance nearly half way around the earth. At the high point

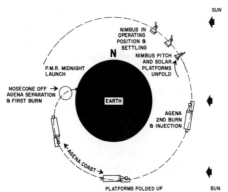

Fig. 10-17. Nimbus launch and orbit injection sequence. (NASA)

(apogee) of this ellipse, additional thrust, to the velocity necessary to retain this altitude as a circular orbit, should be provided by the Agena second burn. This second burn is sometimes referred to as a "kick-in-the-apogee."

For Nimbus, second burn and injection were near local noon, near the island of Madagascar. Unfortunately, the Agena second burn was of less duration than planned, and the Nimbus I orbit was far less circular than desired. Nimbus I orbit parameters were: Apogee—580 statute miles; Perigee—263 statute miles; Eccentricity—0.036; Period—98.3 minutes; and Inclination—98.7° (81.3° retrograde).

After completion of second burn, the Agena is rotated to place the Nimbus in approximately the correct attitude. This conserves the Nimbus gas supply. Then the satellite is separated, using a slight forward thrust of the Nimbus by calibrated springs in the Agena-spacecraft adapter. The Agena turns and gives itself a thrust to the side to be sure it is out of the way of Nimbus. The Nimbus horizon sensors controlled the final attainment of vertical stabilization.

Yaw stabilization was slightly deferred to allow time for vertical (pitch and roll) stabilization. Then the paddles unfolded and the sun sensing devices established initial yaw orientation. This allowed time for total orientation to be established before the Nimbus entered the earth's shadow near the North Pole. At this time, yaw control was automatically transferred from the sun sensor to the gyro.

As the satellite passed over the Fairbanks, Alaska, CDA station, orientation was confirmed, the operating Nimbus subsystems were checked, and operation of selected other subsystems was initiated. In successive orbits, more subsystem check-outs and initiations were commanded until the entire satellite was operating and collecting meteorological data.

Command and Data Acquisition Stations and Procedures

The NASA Command and Data Acquisition (CDA) Station near Fairbanks, Alaska, is the primary site for command of

Fig. 10-18. The Fairbanks CDA station and antenna at Gilmore Creek near Fairbanks, Alaska. (NASA)

the Nimbus satellite and read-out of its data. A second station, near Rossman, N. C., is also used. These stations perform similar functions for other NASA satellites.

The Fairbanks CDA Station can contact about ten of the approximately 14 daily Nimbus orbits. Since Nimbus can store up to two orbits of AVCS and HRIR data, this single station misses only three orbits of data each day.

The Fairbanks and other CDA stations have components analogous to those of the TIROS CDA stations:

(1) An antenna for acquiring the data;

(2) Equipment for causing the antenna to track the satellite;

(3) Devices to command read-out and other satellite functions;

(4) Equipment to record the data acquired;

(5) Devices for any on-site processing of the data, and

(6) Facilities for transmitting the data or the results of its analysis to other points.

The Fairbanks antenna (Figure 10-18) is located in a valley, well away from known sources of radio interference, with the surrounding hills providing additional protection. Before the site was chosen, a radio frequency search was made on the site, and a radio frequency interference (RFI) free zone was established.

The antenna is an 85-foot diameter parabolic dish which focuses the radio energy from the satellite on the actual antenna elements at the apex of the four beams which extend forward of the dish. It is a standard NASA design. It rotates both vertically and horizontally using an X-Y mount. That is, the antenna dish is mounted on two circular structures at right angles to each other. By rotating one or both of these structures, the antenna can point or track in any direction.

An X-Y mount is best for tracking low-level satellites since it can follow a spacecraft even when moving directly overhead. An antenna with an azimuth-elevation mounting, those used at the other TIROS stations, usually cannot rotate through the vertical to the other side. On an overhead pass, it must rapidly slew around to continue tracking as the spacecraft recedes.

To gather maximum energy in high frequencies, such as the Nimbus S-band, the antenna dish must form a very precise, smooth parabola. This requires careful design and a structure that does not distort from varying stresses (different positions) or changing temperatures.

An antenna of this size has a narrow beamwidth. The 85-foot antenna beamwidth is a cone only 6° in diameter at 136 Mcs (the Nimbus beacon frequency) and merely 0.6° at 1700 Mcs (the frequency of the Nimbus S-band transmitter.)

While antenna directions can be manually controlled, such control is seldom sufficiently precise. Normally, tracking is initiated by a controlling computer, using predicted satellite position angles. When the beacon signal is received, the antenna is switched to 136 Mcs auto-track and the beacon signals keep the antenna pointed at Nimbus as it moves over the station. After the satellite S-band transmitter is commanded on, S-band autotracking is used because of its greater precision.

Command of Nimbus during a pass goes as follows:

(1) A command sequence tape is inserted in the CDA

Command Console. This tape is in two parts: the first to confirm proper satellite condition, and the second to direct the read-out sequence and operations during the next orbit.

(2) When the beacon signal is received, the command tape causes the satellite to immediately transmit current engineering telemetry data. The telemetry data are both recorded and fed directly to twin CDC-924 computers. The computers immediately scan the data and notify the station operators if anything is seriously wrong with the satellite.

(3) Assuming this quick-look check finds everything in good shape, the second part of the tape commands readout of the stored engineering telemetry, the AVCS pictures, and the HRIR data. Then, beacon transmission is resumed and the satellite is sent any needed commands. This ends contact with the satellite for that pass.

(4) The various data are recorded on tape, both for sloweddown playback (to match the capabilities of some of the data processing equipments and the communications lines) and to insure copies of the signals are available if data were lost during processing.

(5) The PCM-A data are also fed directly to the computers. Processing of the engineering data is begun while the pass is still in progress.

Processing of the engineering telemetry includes:

(1) Identification of values outside specified limits (too high temperatures, etc.).

(2) Checks of sensors related to those outside limits.

(3) Determination of minimum, average, and maximum values of each telemetry point.

(4) Determination of battery charge and other values critical to future commands.

(5) Preparation of data for analysis at NASA's Goddard Space Flight Center.

(6) Determination of satellite attitude at the time of each AVCS picture.

(7) Calculation of AVCS and HRIR geographical grids, using attitude and orbit data. This may be done either at the CDA station or at Goddard Space Flight Center.

Pertinent information is sent to the Nimbus Technical Control Center (Greenbelt, Maryland) for planning future command sequences. The Nimbus Technical Control Center (NTCC) performs functions analogous to those of the TIROS Technical Control Center.

The tape on which the AVCS pictures are recorded is played-back at one-eighth the recording speed. The picture signals and the grid data (prepared by the computer) are sent to a grid-mixing unit. The pictures are gridded while they are still electrical signals, either at the CDA or GSFC.

The computer calculates where each point on the grid lines will fall in the TV scan, and sorts the points in that order. When the grid mixer sends the picture signals to a kinescope-recorder, it counts until a grid point is reached. It then suppresses the picture and inserts a grid-line dot. The mixer then continues the picture signals and counts to the next grid line point. The entire picture is played-out, combined with the proper grid to show the location of the clouds. This process requires only about thirty minutes for 96 pictures.

The gridded pictures are photographed on a kinescope, much as for the TIROS pictures, and are immediately developed. If the wide band communications line to Washington should fail, the pictures at Fairbanks can be used to prepare emergency nephanalyses, the same as those prepared at the TIROS stations. These nephanalyses can then be sent to Washington on a facsimile line, independent of the wide-band line.

In an emergency, the pictures can be gridded by manual techniques similar to those used with TIROS pictures.

The AVCS pictures are transmitted to the Goddard Space Flight Center over a wide-band 96 Kcs line reserved for Nimbus data. One orbit's pictures can be transmitted in about thirty minutes. From Goddard they are relayed by microwave to the Weather Bureau's National Weather Satellite Center.

The telemetry and HRIR data are also sent to Washington on the Telpak B line. All the data can be transmitted in the period of less than half an orbit, so a backlog should never develop unless there is a line failure.

Summary

One difficulty encountered in any attempt to become familiar with Nimbus, particularly from published sources such as those cited as References, are differences between the original design and Nimbus I (due to changes during development and because of weight limitations), and between these and what is visualized for later Nimbus. The following table should clarify some of these matters.

Comparison of Initial Design for Nimbus, and the First and later Nimbus

	Original Design	Nimbus I	Later Nimbus
Spacecraft Weight	650 pounds	750 pounds	850-1000 pounds
Orbit Altitude	600 nautical miles	500 nautical miles	750 nautical miles
Launch Vehicle	Thor-Agena B	Thor-Agena B	Thorad—or Atlas-Agena D
Stabilization Accuracy	$\pm 1°$	$\pm 2\text{-}3°$	$\pm 1°$
Power in sun-light	450 watts	400 watts	Possible use of SNAP generator (nuclear power)
Engineering Telemetry	Redundant recorder	Single recorder	Redundant recorder
Camera Systems AVCS	Redundant Cameras & recorders	No redundancy	Redundant Cameras & recorders
APT	Redundant	Single Unit	Redundant
Di-electric Tape Camera (Chap. 14)	Experimental Model	Omitted	Experimental model; may later replace AVCS
Radiometers HRIR	1.5 mile resolution	5-mile resolution	Possibly with direct read-out capability
MRIR	Included	Omitted	Included
Scheduled First Launch	Mid-1962	Aug. 1964 (actual)	–

The launch of the second Nimbus, somewhat modified from Nimbus I but not so greatly as in the right-hand column above, is presently planned for the early part of 1966.

The history of Nimbus has made it clear that we still have much to learn about the best ways to organize and manage such large spacecraft projects; and about ways to forecast accurately their schedules and costs. The scheduled launch date for Nimbus slipped from mid-1962 (as established in 1960) to 1963 and then to 1964.

Concurrently with the repeated slippages in the Nimbus schedule, the estimated costs of developing, building and testing the first two Nimbus (not including the cost of their launch vehicles) increased from $17.2 million in early 1961 to over $60 million by the end of 1962. The launch vehicle (Thor-Agena B) costs remained relatively stable at about $6.5 million each.

In spite of the problems and limitations of Nimbus, it is basically a good design and should ultimately play a significant role in satisfying national and world-wide meteorological requirements.

Note. A catalog including copies of all the Nimbus I HRIR data has recently been published (Staff Members, Aeronomy and Meteorology Division, 1965, *Nimbus I High Resolution Radiation Data Catalog and User's Manual*, NASA, Goddard Space Flight Center). An analogous AVCS catalog, but with only samples of the data, is also available.

11

The National Operational Meteorological Satellite System (NOMSS)

A complication throughout the meteorological satellite program has been aptly termed, by a key leader in the program, its "schizophrenia." Schizophrenia refers to a split-personality, as in the Dr. Jekyll-Mr. Hyde case. The "schizophrenia" of the meteorological satellite program has been between its research objectives and its operational meteorological requirements.

It would be a mistake to assume this has been a black or white matter. Even those advocating immediate operational use of the data value a vigorous research program; and those desiring to give research the immediate key role anticipate widespread future operational applications of meteorological satellite data. But differences, while those of emphasis and timing, have been real and significant.

The advocates of emphasizing research have been chiefly, but not exclusively, associated with NASA, although not all NASA personnel have felt this way. They initially opposed immediate operational use of the TIROS data. For example, NASA refused the USWB use of the TIROS data for operational weather analysis for several weeks after the launch of TIROS I. The use within 60 hours of launch was by the U. S. military weather services, whom ARPA insisted be allowed such use.

They felt Nimbus should be fully tested before planning an operational system—although, reluctantly, they did agree to operational use of the Nimbus I data.

The principal advocates of operational applications of meteorological satellite data have been the U. S. Weather Bureau and the military weather services. While admitting that much R&D remains, and that operational plans must minimize interference with research, these weather services insisted that operations be given at least equal priority with R&D. They developed and implemented the operational use of TIROS data. They pushed for early operational use of Nimbus data, and for implementation of an operational system concurrent with spacecraft development.

These two viewpoints are not irreconcilable; there is a middle ground. In any event, these differences should have become moot on May 25, 1961, when the President of the United States recommended immediate development of a National Operational Meteorological Satellite System. Nevertheless, these arguments still complicate the program.

The recommendation of the President stemmed from the dramatic success with which the TIROS I data were operationally applied. This led the Weather Bureau and the military services to request NASA to stop thinking of TIROS and Nimbus as routine research projects, and to consider the urgent development of a truly operational capability.

"On October 10, 1960, top officials of the National Aeronautics and Space Administration, the Department of Commerce (of which USWB is a part), the Federal Aviation Agency, and the Department of Defense, met and decided that the time had come to lay plans for a national operational meteorological satellite system. As a consequence, the Panel on Operational Meteorological Satellites (POMS) was established as an interagency working group under the auspices of the National Coordinating Committee for Aviation Meteorology (NACCAM) and with participation and endorsement of the agencies listed above. POMS was instructed to develop a plan for the operational system . . ." (see Reference 11-G-1). (NACCAM is an interagency group chaired by the Chief of the USWB).

Mr. E. M. Cortwright, NASA, was designated Chairman. Dr. Morris Tepper, Chief, Meteorological Satellite Programs, NASA, served as Secretary. The author participated in the deliberations and in the drafting of the report, entitled "Plan for a National Operational Meteorological Satellite System" (see Reference 11-G-1).

The POMS members began work in December 1960, and their report was submitted in April 1961. They agreed the operational meteorological satellite system should:

(1) Satisfy the meteorological requirements of all the users;

(2) Phase into operation at the earliest date;

(3) Capitalize on the continuing research and development program; and

(4) Serve first the United States, but where possible also serve international needs.

POMS proposed that the system make maximum use of data to be obtained from an augmentation of the NASA Nimbus program to provide an expanded operational capability. Later, independent operational status would be attained. A schematic of the proposed system, used as the Frontispiece to the report, is reproduced as Figure 11-1.

"The initial capability would include both day and night cloud observations, heat balance measurements and direct transmission of local cloud cover data to local weather stations. The observational potential of the system would be increased in accordance with the progress of the supporting NASA research program."

POMS also proposed: ". . . the TIROS program be extended

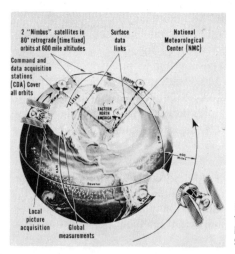

Fig. 11-1.   Schematic of the National Operational Meteorological Satellite System. (NACCAM)

to provide some measure of operational capability prior to the first Nimbus launch."

The POMS plan was favorably reviewed by several government committees. On May 25, 1961, President Kennedy addressed the Congress on "Urgent National Needs" (see Reference 11-G-8). In the Section on Space, he stated (in part):

"I therefore ask the Congress, above and beyond the increases I have earlier requested for space activities, to provide the funds which are needed to meet the following national goals:

"First, I believe that this nation should commit itself to achieving the goal, before this decade is out, of landing a man on the moon and returning him safely to earth. . .

"Fourth, an additional $75 million, of which $53 million is for the Weather Bureau, will help give us at the earliest possible time a satellite system for worldwide weather observation. Such a system will be of inestimable commercial and scientific value; and the information it provides will be made freely available to all the nations of the world."

The Congress carefully considered these recommendations (see Reference 11-G-2), and appropriated $48 million to the Weather Bureau for initiation of NOMSS. While about ten per cent less than requested, it was ample to start.

NASA and the USWB resumed consideration of how best to merge the NOMSS initiation with the Nimbus development program. It was agreed to establish an interim phase "to be designated as the Nimbus Operational System (NOS)." It was further agreed that during this phase, the Weather Bureau would determine the observational requirements; and process, analyze, disseminate, use and archive the data. NASA would design, build, and operate the spacecraft and the CDA stations.

Several items in this agreement turned out to be subject to interpretation. These, related to the "schizophrenia" mentioned earlier, have hampered the harmony and progress of the program.

It was subsequently agreed that NASA would use USWB

funds to construct five operational Nimbus (NOS) spacecraft, scheduled between its four R&D Nimbus. The data from all nine satellites would be available to satisfy the operational requirements of NOMSS. Thereafter, Operational Nimbus would be launched as necessary to meet NOMSS requirements. Further NASA research launches would continue separately.

Because of delays in the first Nimbus launch, the USWB provided funds to NASA for additional TIROS. Two TIROS will be kept in operation, with their orbits coordinated to provide coverage equatorward of about 65° latitude (Chapter 12). This program, the TIROS Operational Satellite System (TOSS) (see Reference 11-1) provides an interim operational capability. (TIROS X was one of these.)

An operational system requires Command and Data Acquisition (CDA) stations. Since the NASA Fairbanks antenna must handle other satellites (such as the Polar Orbiting Geophysical Observatory—POGO), a second antenna to serve NOMSS was built on the same site. A second NOMSS CDA, probably along the east coast of North America or in Europe, will eventually be needed.

From the CDA stations, the NOMSS data are to flow to the National Weather Satellite Center located at Suitland, Maryland. From Fairbanks, wideband 96 Kc Telpak-B links have been installed to allow the NWSC to receive the data in its full fidelity. From any overseas CDA, communications limitations will require partial processing and loss in detail until communications satellites can provide a wide-band capability. The collection and dissemination of weather data of all types will be a major role of a communications satellite system.

The operational meteorological satellite data will be processed at NWSC, as shown in Figure 11-2 (see Reference 11-G-5), more fully described by Bristor (see Reference 11-G-6) and Miller (see Reference 11-G-7). To the left, the data enter the terminal equipment from the Telpak B lines. Control of the data flow and all the processing units is exercised by the semi-automatic control terminal and the system operator, shown at the bottom left. The data are immediately recorded on magnetic tape, both to preserve them in case of

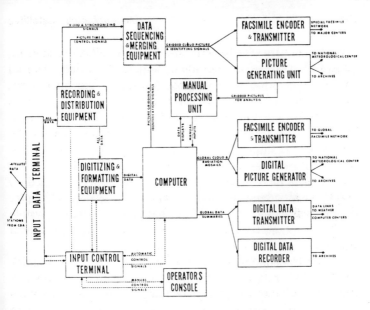

Fig. 11-2. NOMSS data processing system. (USWB)

a malfunction and to allow playbacks at varying speeds where the processing equipments require it. If the pictures were gridded before they came over the Telpak B Line, they are ready for photographic recording or retransmission. If not, gridding is performed in the Data Merging Equipment; the procedure is basically the same as at the CDA station. The gridding computations are performed in the IBM 7094 Computer, the heart of the NOMSS Data Processing System.

The gridded pictures are photographed to provide high quality films for operational analysis at the National Meteorological Center and for research. In parallel with this kinescope recording, pictures of selected areas are processed for transmission by a special facsimile circuit, to major weather centrals in the United States. Similar processing, presentation, and distribution is also planned for the HRIR data.

The pictures and radiation signals are also converted into digital (discrete numerical) formats by the 7094. This is done in the Digitizing and Formatting Equipment, which also loads the digitized data into the 7094 Computer.

The Computer will be aided by analysts, who will indicate areas which are snow and might be mistaken as clouds, and who perform other interpretation functions. Later, the computer will take over additional interpretation functions, but it will be a long time before the human analyst is obsolete. For this reason, the NOMSS processing system is a coordinated man-machine complex.

One function the computer can perform well is rectification (making the data fit standard map projections). It can also summarize the data; providing average values for small areas of cloud cover, cloud brightness, and cloud top height. With such compaction, the data fit facsimile limitations. At first, the human analysts will identify cloud types, cloud line orientations, etc.; later, the computer may handle these as our "know-how" improves. These compacted data, with manual annotations, will serve as improved nephanalyses for transmission over the world. Other copies of these data will go to the NMC for use in analysis and forecasting, and into the archives for research and climatology.

The output of the computer can be sent directly to other computers, both at the NMC and at other computer-equipped weather centrals. There, the data will be used for machine-made weather forecasts as rapidly as techniques can be developed. Stored on tape or film, they can later be used by still other computers for research and climatology.

In summary, the outputs of the NOMSS Data Processing Center will include:

(1) Geographically Located and Gridded Cloud Pictures to:
    a. National Meteorological Center
    b. Major Weather Centrals, for selected areas
    c. Weather Data Archives for R&D

(2) Nephanalyses (probably Rectified, Compacted, and Annotated Pictures) to:
    a. Weather Stations, worldwide
    b. National Meteorological Center
    c. Archives

(3) Rectified and Compacted Pictures to:
    a. National Meteorological Center

   b. Archives
(4) Picture Data in Digital Form to:
   a. NMC Computers
   b. Computers at other weather centrals
   c. Archives for research and climatology

The reduction, processing, and analysis of the data is a complex operation. Because of the perishability of weather data, each orbit's data must be processed before the next one comes in. A backlog cannot be tolerated.

The plan for the NOMSS Data Processing System was developed by NWSC personnel. They were assisted by a contractor, Ess Gee, Inc., of Elmsford, N. Y. The system is analogous to that outlined by the author in 1960 (see Reference 11-2).

When the POMS plan was presented in April, 1961, it was expected the system would be in interim operation in 1962, with Nimbus as its spacecraft. Subsequent delays in Nimbus, and increases in the cost of Nimbus, led the Weather Bureau to consider whether NOMSS should plan to complement or replace Nimbus with a simpler satellite. (Nimbus could, in any event, be used to develop improved sensors and to gather special data for research.) Most reasonable might be the operation of only one Nimbus at a time, providing cloud pictures plus other data which are needed only once or twice a day. More frequent cloud observations (which may be required four to six times a day) and simpler radiometric measurements could be taken by smaller "gap-filler" weather satellites placed in orbits suitable to complement Nimbus observations.

In September 1963, the Weather Bureau announced its decision that "the complexity of the present design of the Nimbus satellite would make its use prohibitively high in cost compared with (1) the value of the data to be obtained, and (2) the resources that could be made available." It canceled its order to NASA for the purchase of five additional Nimbus to be used in NOS.

At about the same time, the agreement with NASA was renegotiated to provide that the Weather Bureau would, in addition to its previous responsibilities, approve and monitor the operational satellite designs and developments, and operate the operational CDA's and satellites after they were successfully in orbit. Under the terms of this agreement, USWB notified NASA of the need for development of an Interim Operational Meteorological Satellite (IOMS) System, to be available in 1965 and later, an advanced operational meteorological satellite system. IOMS, now called TOS, was to be based on TIROS and other current space technology.

While various configurations have been considered for IOMS, currently attracting most attention is a proposal of RCA, originally studied with Navy support, and more recently investigated by the Weather Bureau and subsequently by NASA. For reasons that will develop, this configuration is often referred to as a "Cartwheel" or "Wheel" satellite.

The Cartwheel would look much like a TIROS. However, the camera or cameras would point out through the curved sides, rather than out the flat base plate as in the case of the first eight TIROS. The cameras might be individual snapshot (with storage on magnetic tape) vidicons essentially the same as in TIROS, the Automatic Picture Transmission (APT) type, or combinations thereof.

The satellite would be oriented in orbit with the spin axis perpendicular to the plane of the orbit. The satellite, as it spun, would appear to roll along the orbit. With the satellite so oriented, each camera would point vertically down (or nearly so) for an instant once each revolution of the satellite. Satellite spin would be about the same as TIROS—10 rpm.

The satellite would be kept in the proper attitude by a sophisticated magnetic orientation control coil system. The current through the coil must vary over particular locations, twice each orbit as against the once every few days for TIROS. Accordingly, the coil must be programmed through a command-clock subsystem. This complexity is made necessary by the pattern of the earth's magnetic field.

To take pictures from such a spacecraft, the cameras must snap only when they are pointing most nearly straight down, but not as frequently as every spin, which would provide excessive overlap. A combination of a timer and a horizon scanning system is used. After the proper interval from the last picture, the timer would arm the camera shutter, which would then be triggered by a horizon scanning system the next time the camera was pointing down.

The ninth TIROS was modified to a "Wheel" configuration. It carries two TIROS wide-angle cameras, pointed in opposite directions 63½° to the spin axis (Figure 11-3) or 26½° to the vertical when pointing most nearly down. Each is triggered at times when its axis is closest to the vertical. The combined fields of view of the two cameras cover a horizon-to-horizon strip along the orbit. A modified array of horizon scanners provide improved spin axis attitude information and trigger the cameras at the proper times. Otherwise, the equipment is much the same as in earlier TIROS. The ninth TIROS was placed in a 2:30 sun-synchronous quasi-polar orbit.

TIROS IX was successfully launched from Cape Kennedy into a quasi-polar orbit on January 22, 1965. Due to an excessive period of second stage thrust, it went into a very elliptical orbit with a perigee of 435 statute miles and an apogee of 1603 statute miles. This unplanned orbit has complicated the testing of the wheel mode of operation, but in general the performance in this mode has been successful. It is expected, however, that the wide range of orbit altitudes will provide an unplanned bonus as an opportunity to investigate optimum meteorological satellite altitudes (see Chapter 12).

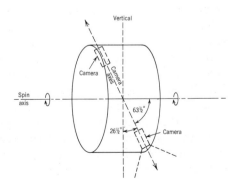

Fig. 11-3. Camera orientations in the TIROS "Wheel."

The Cartwheel configuration is equally usable in any type of orbit—inclined, polar, or equatorial—although the areas of coverage vary with the orbit. Used with an APT camera, the Cartwheel configuration is often referred to as a Direct Readout Weather Satellite or DROWS (see Reference 11-3). When used in an equatorial orbit, it is sometimes referred to as DREWS (Direct Readout Equatorial Weather Satellite).

The Cartwheel configuration provides the daytime cloud coverage expected of Nimbus. To increase the satellite's utility, radiometric scanning observations, especially of nighttime cloud cover, would be highly desirable. The scan cannot come directly from the satellite's rotation, as in TIROS; this only produces a scan along the orbit, not across it.

The author has proposed a method for scanning from a Cartwheel configuration. The radiometer optics would be mounted with the optical axis coincident with the spacecraft spin axis (see Figure 11-4), and could be like those in the Nimbus HRIR. However, rather than the rotating mirror of HRIR, a servo motor would hold a 45° mirror to deflect the field of view of the radiometer radially in the vertical. At the rim of the satellite, the field of view would be further diverted by helical mirrors, to scan across the earth from horizon to horizon at a rate chosen to provide complete coverage.

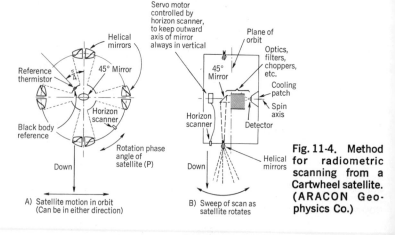

A) Satellite motion in orbit (Can be in either direction)

B) Sweep of scan as satellite rotates

Fig. 11-4. Method for radiometric scanning from a Cartwheel satellite. (ARACON Geophysics Co.)

12

Some Orbits of Particular Meteorological Significance

The reasons a satellite stays in orbit have been abundantly explained in other books. So have the geometric factors of an orbit: its elliptical shape; decrease of orbit velocity and increase of period with increasing altitude; spin of the earth under the orbit so the orbit appears to move westward 15° per hour relative to the earth, etc.

But there are aspects of particular meteorological significance that deserve discussion.

With rare exceptions, it is desirable that a meteorological satellite orbit be as close to circular as possible. Orbit circularity aids data reduction in two ways:

(1) The area and scale of each picture remain constant.

(2) The subpoint of the satellite always travels over the earth at the same rate. Orbit prediction and location calculations are simplified.

Because the earth (in common with more than a few meteorologists) has a slight bulge at its equator, an orbit does not remain fixed in space; rather, the plane of the orbit rotates slowly around the earth's axis, when considered from the viewpoint of the sun and the fixed stars (see Reference 12-1). This rotation determines where there is enough sun illumination for cloud pictures. The orbit plane precesses a few degrees per day in Right Ascension (astronomical longitude). Detailed descriptions of this precession and its rate, which depends on orbit inclination and altitude, can be found in several sources (such as Reference 12-G-1). The precession is analogous to the horizontal rotation of a gyroscope axis when suspended by one end, or to the wobble of a spinning top when the axis tilts away from the vertical.

The precession is directed opposite to the motion of the satellite in orbit. For a satellite moving from west to east, the precession is from east to west; and vice versa for a retrograde orbit.

Approximate values of orbit precession, *in absolute space,* for TIROS and Nimbus orbits are:

Satellite	Orbit Altitude	Orbit Inclination	Approx. precession (in absolute space)
TIROS	400 miles	48°	5° per day (westward)
TIROS	400 miles	58°	4° per day (westward)
Nimbus	600 nautical miles	80° (retrograde)	1° per day (eastward)

These orbital precessions are relative only to absolute space, or the fixed stars. Precession *relative to the sun* determines illumination for satellite photography. *Relative to the sun,* an orbit with no *absolute* precession (a purely polar orbit) would appear to precess from east-to-west at about one degree a day, due to the movement of the earth in its orbit around the sun. The exact rate is $\frac{360}{365}$ or 0.9856 degrees per day. In three months, a satellite in a noon and midnight polar orbit would appear to have rotated 90° relative to the sun, and to be a "dawn-dusk" orbit.

To consider illumination, absolute and "solar" precessions must be algebraically added to get the apparent total precession relative to the sun. Its approximate values are:

Satellite	Orbit Altitude	Orbit Inclination	Approx. precession (relative to sun)
TIROS	400 miles	48°	6° per day (westward)
TIROS	400 miles	58°	5° per day (westward)
Nimbus	600 nautical miles	80° (retrograde)	0° per day

These orbit precession principles determine why a single TIROS cannot give complete coverage, and why the areas of coverage vary from week to week. The following discussion is adapted from a paper by Wood and the author (see Reference 12-2).

A number of factors limit the areas over which TIROS can make observations. Inclination of the orbit, the solar illumina-

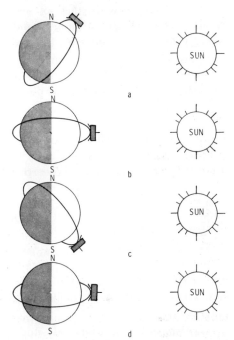

Fig. 12-1.   Precession of the TIROS orbit plane. (NASA)

tion needed for photography, data storage capabilities, and camera attitude have been discussed earlier (Chapter 5). Two other factors, precession of the orbit and the locations of the data read-out stations, are more subtle.

Latitude limitations to coverage are due to the need for solar illumination and a consequence of orbit precessions. One cycle of the precession of the orbit plane, relative to the sun, is completed in about nine weeks for a 48° TIROS orbit and in slightly over ten weeks for a 58° orbit. In this discussion, the 48° orbit usually will be used to illustrate the points discussed.

During a single day, the plane of the orbit remains nearly fixed in absolute space and relative to the sun, while the earth rotates independently within the orbit. (A globe of the earth will help in understanding these matters. The Rand

McNally *Satellite,* which has an extra ring that simulates a satellite orbit and can be tilted to any inclination, is especially useful.) From the viewpoint only of illumination, the same latitudes at all longitudes can be observed by the cameras at various times during one 24-hour period. However, the locations of the readout stations place an additional constraint on observable longitudes (see later section). The slow precession of the orbit plane causes the illuminated latitudes, as seen from the satellite, to change over a nine-week cycle.

TIROS launch time is so chosen that the northern part of the orbit is on the side of the earth nearest the sun (Figure 12-1) and the TV cameras obtain data over latitudes from about the equator to 50° N latitude (to about 65° for a 58° orbit). At this time, the satellite is over the southern hemisphere only at night. The high noon point of the orbit moves slowly southward until, about one week after launch, the descending node—the point where the orbit crosses the equator on the southbound leg—is on the same side of the earth as the sun. At this time, photographic observations are made between approximately 35° N and 35° S latitude.

Precession of the orbit and southward movement of the illuminated area under the orbit continue until, about 3½ weeks after launch, the southern part of the orbit is nearest the sun. Photographic data are obtained between about 20°-50° S latitude; but not in the northern hemisphere, over which the satellite now passes only at night. From this point, precession causes the illuminated portion of the orbit to gradually move northward; about six weeks after launch, the ascending node—the point where the orbit crosses the equator on the north-bound leg—is on the same side of the earth as the sun. Again observable latitudes are primarily in the tropics. Continued precession and northward movement of the illuminated area reach the point, about eight weeks after launch, where the northernmost portion is again nearest the sun and photographic observations again are possible between 20°-50° N latitude. Precession continues and now southward movement of the illuminated area under the orbit begins again, with the whole cycle repeating about every nine weeks.

Within the illuminated latitude zone, there are longitude limitations to the areas from which data may be obtained. The locations of the read-out stations (Virginia and California) determine these limitations because:

(1) The data storage capability of the satellite is limited, and

(2) The range at which each station can usefully read-out data is limited to line of sight.

(The subsequently added Alaska read-out station eliminates some longitudinal gaps, but not all, since most of its orbits are the same as for either Viriginia or California.)

When plotted on a Mercator map (Figure 12-2) the 48° orbit describes a sine-shaped curve, centered on the equator with a 48° half-amplitude (in latitude) and a wavelength of about 335° of longitude. The 335° wavelength derives from the rotation of the earth; the longitude of each ascending node is displaced approximately 25° west of that for the preceding orbit. The range of each data read-out station is a circle with a radius of about 20° of latitude.

Orbits with ascending nodes over the Atlantic Ocean cannot be contacted by either read-out station; the first orbit that can has an ascending node of about 75° W longitude (Orbit A, Figure 12-2). The next seven orbits can also be contacted by either or both of the Virginia or California stations, the last one being that with an ascending node near 80° E (Orbit B). During this 7½-orbit period, station locations impose no limit on the data obtained. The area covered during this 7½-orbit period, defined as Area I, is the most favorable for photographic coverage.

During the approximately 6½-orbits between the last contact with the California station and the next with the Virginia station (about 24 hours after Orbit A, Figure 12-2) TIROS can obtain:

(1) A single sequence of 32 pictures from each of the cameras.

(2) Infrared radiation data for the last 100 minutes before the Virginia contact.

The areas covered during this 6½ orbit period, Areas II

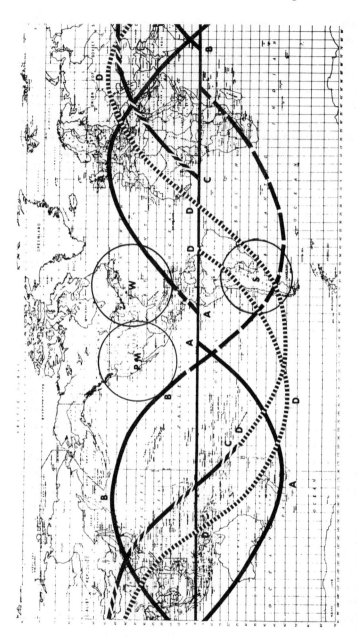

Fig. 12-2.   48° orbit subpoint traces. (NASA)

and III (defined below), are less favorable for photographic coverage.

An additional factor further limits the data obtained during this 6½ orbit period of time. The satellite clocks, which determine when remote picture sequences start, can run for a maximum of only three orbits (five hours) after being started (see Chapter 5). Under normal operating modes, this limits picture data, following the last California contact, to the area between this contact (just before the descending node on Orbit B) and five hours and 15 minutes later (shortly after the descending node on Orbit C). The area covered during this three-orbit (five-hour) period is Area II (Figure 12-3a, 3b). From this point, no pictures could be taken under normal operating modes, until the first Virginia contact.

To overcome this limitation, a supplemental mode is used. The clocks are set during the last California contact (Orbit B), but are started by a special signal from the NASA Minitrack Station at Santiago, Chile. This permits pictures to be taken between the time an orbit comes within range of Santiago (such as Orbit D) and the next contact with the Virginia station. The area over which pictures can be taken using the Santiago clock start is Area III (Figure 12-3a, 3b).

The special mode can in no way increase the amount of data that are obtained during the 6½-orbit time period (Areas II and III) following the last California contact; it only permits more flexibility in choosing the areas over which the pictures are taken.

An area over central, southern and southeastern Eurasia, and another over the southeastern Pacific Ocean and southern Argentina and southern Chile are always in either Area II or Area III. The amount of data that TIROS can obtain over these areas is severely limited.

In many parts of the world, the period of southbound passes is more favorable than that of northbound passes, or vice versa. To determine this, the maps (Figures 12-3a and 12-3b) are used. Area I is the most favorable; next most favorable is Area II. Area III provides the least favorable probability of obtaining pictures from the satellite.

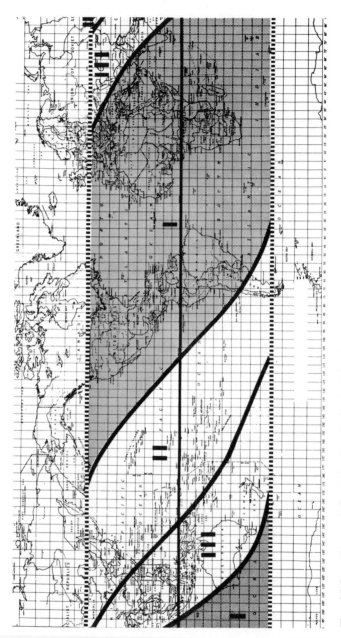

Fig. 12-3a. Areas defined by longitudinal limitations, southbound passes. (NASA)

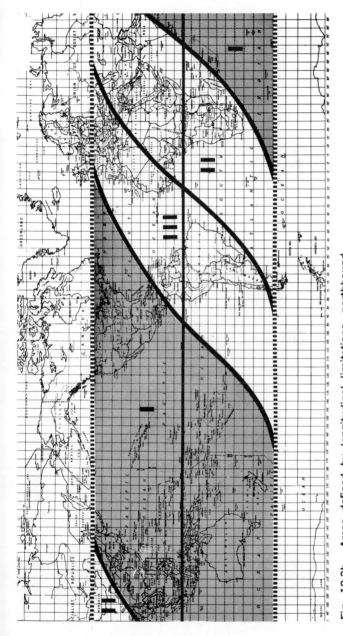

Fig. 12-3b. Areas defined by longitudinal limitations, northbound passes. (NASA)

Consider the part of Brazil between the equator and 30° S latitude. On the southbound portions of the orbits, parts of the area are under an illuminated portion of the orbit from shortly after launch until about the 26th day after launch and again from about the 65th to the 90th day. On the northbound portion of the orbits, parts of the area are under an illuminated portion of the orbit from about the 23rd to the 46th day and again starting about the 87th day. However, Brazil is under Area I (most favorable conditions) for southbound portions of the orbit while it is under Area III (least favorable conditions) for northbound portions. Accordingly, the most favorable periods for TIROS pictures over Brazil would be during the two 16-day periods centered about the 12th and 76th days after launch, when Brazil is under an illuminated southbound portion of the orbit.

The graphs and maps are for a nominal TIROS orbit (380 nautical mile altitude; 48.5° inclination). They are approximately valid for the orbits attained by TIROS I, II, III, and IV. As TIROS V, VI, VII, and VIII were launched into higher inclination (58°) orbits, adjustments are necessary due to the poleward extension of the viewable latitudes and the change of the rate of orbital precession. But the principles are the same. TIROS IX and X, however, are in quasi-polar orbits.

There are potential variations in the boundaries in the graphs and maps of 25° in longitude and 6° in latitude. Longitude may vary because of differences in the position of the first and/or the last orbits that can be interrograted by the read-out stations. Both the longitude and latitude may vary dependent upon satellite attitude, as programmed using the magnetic coil.

More accurate photographic programming information is usually placed on international meteorological communications networks seven days in advance and again 24-48 hours in advance.

It is at times possible to obtain limited pictures north of 48° N and south of 48° S, the extreme orbital subpoints. (58° for TIROS V and subsequent. Useful data to latitudes of 65° have been obtained in many cases.) However, the probability of data being obtained decreases when proceeding poleward of these latitudes.

For Nimbus, and other meteorological satellites in a polar orbit (such as the Wheel TIROS), it is generally agreed that it is best if the orbit plane is at a fixed angle to the sun (sun-synchronous); that is, zero precession relative to the sun or 0.9856 degrees per day eastward precession in absolute space. This provides data for each area at the same local times each day. With proper initial injection into orbit, it prevents drifting into an orbit along the sunrise-sunset (dawn-dusk) line (or "earth terminator," as an analogy to lunar illumination terminology). There, the strong illumination contrasts would make photography difficult.

For a single satellite in a quasi-polar orbit, the noon-midnight orbit (equator crossings at local noon and midnight) seems best. It provides maximum daylight illumination, and data approximately representative of average daytime and average nighttime conditions. For two satellites simultaneously in orbit, three AM-three PM and nine AM-nine PM local time orbit orientations would provide equal spacing between observations, and avoid a dawn-dusk orbit. For three satellites, four AM-four PM, noon-midnight, and eight AM-eight PM local time orbits would seem optimum. For this last case, a Nimbus in the noon-midnight orbit and a lesser capability "gap-filler" (such as a TIROS Wheel) in the four and eight orbits would seem a desirable combination.

Zero precession relative to the sun (0.9856 degrees per day eastward precession in absolute space) requires one of the following combinations of orbit altitudes and inclinations or their equivalent:

Orbit Altitude (Nautical Miles)	Orbit Inclination (Retrograde)
450	81.4°
500	81.0°
600	80.1°
750	78.8°

(See Reference 12-1). All of these allow the AVCS and HRIR

sensors to view the pole on each orbit. For Nimbus, orbit drift should not exceed 20° during the first six months in orbit. Twenty degrees is equal to a change in observation time of about 1⅓ hours.

While a sun-synchronous, quasi-polar orbit is generally preferred from the observational viewpoint, Pyle and Singer (see Reference 12-3) have shown that, from the view of command and data acquisition: "A single station at temperate or subpolar latitudes below 69° can never acquire data from every daily pass of an orbit with sun-synchronous inclination, regardless of satellite altitude . . . A station at 65° latitude (Fairbanks, Alaska) can acquire data from every pass of a (non-sun-synchronous) 90°-polar orbit at all altitudes above 550 nautical miles." The relatives priorities to be assigned the observational advantages of the sun-synchronous quasi-polar orbit as against the data read-out advantages of the exactly polar orbit (with its 1° per day net solar precession) are not yet resolved.

The passes of a polar or quasi-polar orbit have a maximum separation at the equator. For limited fields of camera view or low orbit altitudes, there could be coverage gaps at low latitudes. In any event low latitudes areas midway between orbits are seen only at low resolution and a poor angle. Cowan, Hubbard, and Singer (see Reference 12-4) have suggested the ultimate operational system might include a meteorological satellite (perhaps a Wheel) in an equatorial (0° inclination) orbit to fill these gaps. A recent system engineering project at MIT (see Reference 12-5) featured the student design of a rather excellent, gravity-gradient stabilized, meteorological satellite designed for an equatorial orbit (see Chapter 14).

Many local but severe weather systems have very limited lifetimes. Tornadoes, thunderstorms, thunderstorm complexes and squall lines have typical lifetimes (Figure 12-4) of less than one to only a few hours. Such storms may form, do their damage, and die during the twelve-hour periods between the passes of a single Nimbus, or even the six-hour period for two Nimbus. In many cases, they may exist less than the four-

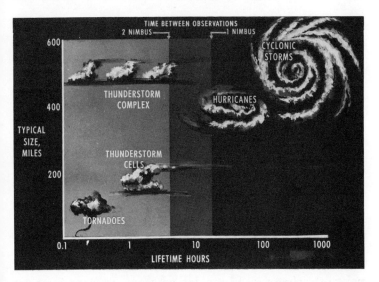

Fig. 12-4.   Lifetimes of typical weather systems. (NASA)

hour interval for three Nimbus or other similar satellites. A way to make the nearly continuous observations necessary to detect and usefully forecast such storms is needed.

As the orbit altitude of a satellite increases, the period of orbit revolution also increases. This is due to a combination of lower orbiting velocity, and the greater orbital distance to be traveled; at about 22,300 miles, the orbit period is exactly twenty-four hours. A satellite at such an altitude, in an equatorial orbit, would appear to stand still over a point on the equator. It could continually view about one-quarter of the temperate and tropical areas of the earth. Three or four such "synchronous" satellites, as they are called (SYNCOM is an experimental Synchronous Communications Satellite), could provide continuous coverage of all tropical and temperate areas. While synchronous satellites in equatorial orbits cannot see the polar areas, the convergence of polar orbits in these areas automatically provides frequent coverage.

The feasibility of a Synchronous Meteorological Satellite (SMS), often referred to as Aeros, is under study by NASA (see References 12-6, 3-1). SMS will be further discussed in Chapter 14.

If desired, a Synchronous satellite could be placed in an inclined orbit. In this case, it would execute an elongated Figure "8" once a day, relative to the earth, centered on the equator and a fixed longitude, with the top and bottom of the "8" at latitudes equal to the inclination of the orbit. Such an orbit could provide improved daytime views of the North American area, but less daytime southern hemisphere data and nighttime northern hemisphere data. Two inclined synchronous satellites, at about the same longitudes but with opposite phasing, would complement each other's coverage.

A further refinement would be an inclined *eccentric* orbit with a mean orbit altitude of 22,300 miles. Because orbit velocity is inversely proportional to orbit altitude, the spacecraft would spend most of its orbit period near apogee (the highest point of the orbit) and relatively little near perigee (the low point), where it is moving fastest. An inclined eccentric synchronous meteorological satellite with both its apogee and its daytime phase in the northern hemisphere (and a mean longitude of say 90-100° W) would provide maximum continuous daytime coverage of the North America area.

To aid its Synchronous Meteorological Satellite feasibility studies, NASA hopes to place a TIROS in an eccentric orbit with an apogee of about 3000 miles and a perigee of 300 miles (see Reference 12-6). This will provide data from altitudes significantly higher than any so far obtained, and pictures of the entire disk of the earth. (Dr. Wexler's schematic, shown in Figure 4-2, shows what might be expected.) A problem here was the number of cameras and the lenses needed to take useful pictures at all altitudes between the perigee and apogee altitudes. Near apogee, the TIROS wide or medium angle lens can photograph the entire disk of the earth, while the narrow angle lens would provide pictures equivalent to those from a normal TIROS. Near perigee, the wide or medium lens can play its normal role. But, at intermediate altitudes, the wide or medium angle cameras would provide insufficient resolution, while the narrow angle would provide inadequate coverage.

The solution to this apparent dilemma again lies in the equatorial bulge of the earth. Not only does it cause the plane of an orbit to precess; it causes rotation *within its plane* of an eccentric orbit. For an inclination of less than 60°, this rotation is in the same direction as the motion of the satellite. Thus, the point of apogee (and, of course, also perigee) slowly but constantly changes both latitude and Right Ascension (astronomical longitude). Further details on precession of the *Argument of Perigee,* as this rotation is called, can be found in, for example, King-Hele (see Reference 12-G-1).

The author suggested (see References 12-7, -8) finding a suitable combination of perigee-apogee altitudes (near 300 and 3000 miles) and orbit inclination such that the forward precession (relative to the sun) of the Argument of Perigee would just equal and counteract the retrograde precession (also relative to the sun) of the orbit plane. In such an orbit, an apogee initially on the same side of the earth as the sun (i.e., where the satellite crossed the longitude of local noon), would always remain in this location. The sunlit portion of the earth would then always be within view of the satellite when it was at apogee. This idea is known as the *Constant Sunlit Apogee Concept.* The cameras would be needed only near apogee; the relatively slow apogee velocity would make a long observation period available. This would provide data on the short period changes of cloud patterns.

Mr. C. P. Wood of NASA's Goddard Space Flight Center investigated this suggestion and found a Constant Sunlit Apogee could be attained with the following orbit parameters (see References 12-7, -8):

> Perigee— 300 nautical miles
> Apogee—3000 nautical miles
> Inclination—36°

A 36° latitude and a 3000-mile altitude permits taking pictures to latitudes of 70°. The Constant Sunlit Apogee concept has done much to assist planning for the highly eccentric TIROS experiment.

There have been several other studies of the optimum orbit altitudes for meteorological satellite observations; only their general results will be summarized here.

Cooper (see Reference 12-9) has shown that, from the viewpoint of coverage, there is little advantage in orbit altitudes above 4000 miles; resolution is generally better at lower altitudes but more uniform near 4000 miles. It is interesting to recall that Wexler suggested this altitude in his pioneering 1954 and 1957 papers (see References 4-5, -7).

Cowan, Hubbard, and Singer (see Reference 12-4) and Gray and Singer (see Reference 12-10) have suggested that (considering such factors as coverage, resolution, minimization of gaps, location errors, satellite altitude, and picture format) the highest "worth" is obtained from a satellite in a 1500 nautical mile polar orbit. At such an altitude, however, other factors not yet included in these studies (launch vehicle capabilities, and the radiation damage in the Van Allen belts) must also be considered. The best altitudes for meteorological satellites, all factors considered, deserve further study.

13

International Cooperation

There are few areas where international cooperation is as cordial and complete as in meteorology. Except during wars, exchange of meteorological data throughout the world is routine. Factors limiting such exchanges are technical or economic, not political or diplomatic.

The reasons do not lie in unusually favorable traits of meteorologists; this cooperation derives from the global nature of the atmosphere.

This atmospheric disregard for national boundaries has been vividly typified by Professor George R. Stewart in his most interesting novel, *Storm* (see Reference 13-1):

"About midnight the (severe cold) front approached the international boundary just north of Havre, Montana. No immigration officers demanded passports; no customs officials searched for contraband. Although the Weather Bureau had given warning, not even a hastily mobilized regiment of the National Guard held the border. At the very least, the Department of State might have sent a sharp note to Ottawa, warning that the Dominion Government would be held strictly accountable for damage done by the Canadian air.

"Reasonable expectation could only be that a hundred or more citizens of the United States would lose their lives in the cold wave, and that wreckage of property would reach millions. Indirectly, through pneumonia and other means, the loss of life would run into many hundreds and the sum of such items as increased consumption of fuel, snow-removal, and delays in transportation would total an appalling figure. Yet the United States of America (often called by its citizens the greatest nation on earth) merely cowered before the Canadian invasion."

The history of international meteorological cooperation was described by Dr. Reichelderfer, former Chief of the U. S. Weather Bureau and from 1951 to 1955, President of the World Meteorological Organization:

"A meeting of prominent meteorologists from many countries was convened in Brussels in 1853 to agree on standards and exchange of weather reports. In 1878 the International Meteorological Organization was formed . . ."

"In 1951, the IMO was transformed into the World Meteorological Organization (WMO), incident to the growing emphasis on affiliation of all intergovernment organizations with the United Nations" (see Reference 13-G-1).

Obviously a global meteorological data-gathering system, such as a satellite, would be of great interest to the WMO. This interest was expressed prior to the launch of TIROS I.

The first cooperation concerning meteorological satellites did not, however, involve the WMO. The author, then with the U. S. Air Force's Cambridge Research Center, and Lt. Col. A. Trakowski, European Office, Air Research and Development Command, arranged in 1958 for studies of cloud systems, as they might appear from a satellite, by Prof. Frank H. Ludlam, Imperial College of Science and Technology, London (see Reference 13-2).

Later the WMO appointed Dr. Harry Wexler of the U. S. Weather Bureau a rapporteur for meteorological satellites (see References 13-3, -4). In 1959, the WMO established a Panel of Experts on Artificial Satellites, with members from the United States (Dr. Wexler), the Soviet Union, the WMO Commission for Aerology, and the WMO Commission for Synoptic Meteorology. The Panel met in November 1959 and February 1961. Its effectiveness was hampered by the absence of a Soviet delegate.

The success of TIROS I led to planning an international program associated with subsequent TIROS. The meteorological services of 21 countries adhering to COSPAR (Committee on Space Research, a committee of the International Council of Scientific Unions (ICSU) were offered satellite orbital information if they wished to make special observations correlated with satellite observations over their locality. Seventeen countries indicated they planned to participate in this program, which never fully materialized due to the degraded pictures of TIROS II. However, a similar program, expanded to invite approximately a hundred countries adhering to WMO, was initiated for TIROS III. Over 30 countries indicated intentions to participate.

With subsequent TIROS, these research programs have become routine.

Samples of TIROS I cloud pictures were presented to foreign meteorological services. Many research papers, presented at the 1962 International Symposium on Rocket and Satellite Meteorology, resulted from these data, and the coordinated observing program (see Reference 13-G-6).

International operational uses of TIROS data were discussed in Chapter 8. So favorable was the response that, in 1962, the U. S. Weather Bureau began overseas radio-facsimile broadcasts of the TIROS nephanalyses.

To further aid the foreign weather services, NASA and the USWB in 1961 presented an International Meteorological Satellite Workshop (see Reference 13-G-2). Twenty-seven nations, as well as international scientific organizations, sent over 100 meteorologists to the workshop. The foreign participants were greatly interested, particularly those from foreign countries having limited weather facilities (see Reference 13-G-7).

In the meantime, events were taking place at the highest diplomatic levels. On September 25, 1961, President Kennedy laid before the United Nations a program including a worldwide undertaking in weather forecasting and weather research.

"A resolution embodying the President's program was unanimously approved by the U. N. General Assembly on December 20, (1961)" (see Reference 13-G-4).

Part C of that Resolution 1721 (XVI) on the *Peaceful Uses of Outer Space* (see Reference 13-G-5), reads in part:
   "The General Assembly"—
   "1. *Recommends* to all Member States and to the World Meteorological Organization and other appropriate specialized

agencies the early and comprehensive study, in the light of developments in outer space, of measures:

"(a) To advance the state of atmospheric science and technology so as to provide greater knowledge of basic physical forces affecting climate and the possibility of large scale weather modification;

"(b) To develop existing weather forecasting capabilities and help Member States make effective use of such capabilities through regional meteorological centres."

It also requested the World Meteorological Organization to prepare a report on these matters, with a view to their further consideration by the General Assembly at its seventeenth session.

The WMO was quick to respond to this challenge. It arranged for two experts, Dr. Harry Wexler of the USA and Prof. Victor Bugaev of the USSR, to draft the requested report. This was one of Dr. Wexler's last major contributions prior to his untimely death. (see Reference 13-7).

The *First Report on the Advancement of Atmospheric Sciences and Their Application in the Light of Developments in Outer Space* (see Reference 13-G-3) was approved in June 1962. Its recommendations included:

(1) The formation of a World Weather Watch to ensure availability to each country of the data best suited to its needs.

(2) Establishing World and Regional Centres, filling the main gaps in the world network of conventional meteorological observing stations, and improved telecommunications facilities, particularly facsimile. Data from meteorological satellites do not make redundant the existing network of meteorological stations. On the contrary, improved networks are needed if maximum benefit is to be derived from satellite data.

(3) The possibility that a satellite might be able to collect information from automatic weather stations and transmit this information to read-out stations (see Chapter 14).

(4) Continued development of techniques for full exploitation of satellite and conventional data, both in research and forecasting.

(5) The need for the consequences of large-scale inter-

ferences with the atmosphere being accurately evaluated in advance.

The favorable reaction of the United Nations to this WMO report is obvious from U. N. General Assembly Resolution 1802 (XVII), December 1962, which reads in part that the U. N.:

"1. *Notes* with appreciation the prompt initial response of the World Meteorological Organization to the request of the General Assembly, as embodied in Resolution 1721 (XVI), that it report on a programme to advance atmospheric science research and to develop improved weather forecasting capabilities in the light of developments in outer space."

The General Assembly then called on the countries of the world, the World Meteorological Organization, the International Council of Scientific Unions, and appropriate United Nations agencies to continue the planning and implementation of expanded meteorological research and improved weather service.

In June 1964, the WMO Executive Committee set the objectives of the program as (1) systematic and standardized global observation through meteorological satellites, various mobile devices for atmosphere sounding and land stations; (2) timely and coordinated dissemination of weather data by all participating countries; (3) processing of data, analyses, and forecasts by a system of world, regional, and national centers. The Committee requested that the national weather services participate in designing a world weather program.

Meanwhile, the United States has been considering the part it should play in this global expansion of meteorological activities. In 1962, the President of the National Academy of Sciences, Dr. Detlev W. Bronk, appointed a Committee on International Programs in Atmospheric Sciences and Hydrology (CIPASH) (see Reference 13-G-8) to develop a proposal. The Academy's proposal was to represent the views of American scientists, provide advice to United States Government Agencies, and serve as a basis for international discussions with interested scientists.

The report of CIPASH, *An Outline of International Programs in the Atmospheric Sciences* (see Reference 13-G-8), was issued in January 1963. It recommended an extensive program which covered such diverse areas as:

(1) Research on Weather Prediction and Modification

(2) Studies of the High Atmosphere

(3) Atmospheric Chemistry

(4) Climatology and Its Long Period Changes

(5) Education and Training

(6) Meteorological Services—Observations (for both research studies and operational forecasts) and Forecasting

(7) Inter-relations with Hydrology and Oceanography

The author was a member of the Panel on Meteorological Services of CIPASH. In cooperation with other members of CIPASH and its panels (especially Dr. Robert White, now Chief of the U. S. Weather Bureau, and Mr. Vincent Lally of the National Center for Atmospheric Research), he was instrumental in recommending:

"Satellites provide us with a surveillance and communications capability whereby unmanned devices, fixed or free-floating in the atmosphere or the oceans, can be interrogated for geophysical information" (see Chapter 14).

"One of the promising developments in the field of unmanned devices is the super-pressure balloon. . . . Under the continuous surveillance of satellites, the locations of the balloons can be determined at desired intervals, thus providing wind observations, in addition to measuring pressure, temperature, humidity, ozone, and other atmospheric variables.

". . . Data obtained by such balloons can provide a substantial portion of the necessary description of the macro-scale state of the atmosphere.

"Neither satellites nor the floating-balloon observing systems will eliminate the need for conventional vertical soundings. *Such soundings will be needed to provide a standard against which other techniques must be measured.*"

Based on the recommendations of the WMO and of CIPASH, the U. S. Weather Bureau is now designing a World Weather System, with special emphasis on the large-scale aspects of the atmosphere. Such aspects, vital to improved meteorological services, can be adequately investigated only by an international cooperative program.

Paralleling these multi-lateral United Nations discussions, the United States and the USSR were engaged in bilateral discussions which included meteorological satellites. On March 7, 1962, President Kennedy, in a letter to former Chairman Khrushchev, stated:

"Perhaps we could render no greater service to mankind through our space programs than by the joint establishment of an early operational weather satellite system. Such a system would be designed to provide global weather data for prompt use by any nation. To initiate this service, I propose that the United States and the Soviet Union each launch a satellite to photograph cloud cover and provide other agreed meteorological service for all nations. The two satellites would be placed in near-polar orbits in planes approximately perpendicular to each other, thus providing regular coverage of all areas. This immensely valuable data would then be disseminated through normal international meteorological channels and would make a significant contribution to the research and service programs now under study by the World Meteorological Organization in response to Resolution 1721 (XVI) adopted by the United Nations Assembly on December 20, 1961."

In his reply of March 20, 1962 to President Kennedy, Mr. Khrushchev stated:

"It is difficult to overestimate the advantage that people would derive from the organization of a worldwide weather observation service using artificial earth satellites. Precise and timely weather predictions would be still another important step on the path to man's subjugation of the forces of nature; it would permit him to combat more successfully the calamities of the elements, and would give new prospects for advancing the well-being of mankind. Let us also cooperate in this field."

In 1962, Dr. Hugh L. Dryden, NASA Deputy Administrator, and Academician A. A. Blagonravov of the Soviet Academy of Sciences met to discuss these matters. In March 1963, they met again with appropriate advisors. The agreements reached fell into two stages: first, the establishment of communication links adequate for the transfer of meteorological satellite data, and later, coordinated launchings of a system of operational weather satellites.

Other international meteorological satellite aspects include: (1) the probability that CDA stations will be established outside the United States, perhaps first in Canada and Europe, and (2) the great international interest in the Automatic Picture Transmission (APT) System. Local cloud pictures will be immediately available to properly equipped weather stations. It should be a particular boon to foreign countries with only limited conventional observations. Several foreign countries already have the necessary stations.

With the cost to the United States of meteorological satellite developments, it may appropriately be questioned whether foreign nations fully appreciate the assistance these satellites are providing. It has been repeatedly demonstrated they do. During 1962, the Australian Meteorological Service itself paid for radio facsimile to insure receiving TIROS data.

Dr. Kaare Langlo, Chief, Technical Division, World Meteorological Organization, has stated (see Reference 13-G-2):

"I think every country, and the Organization itself, is indeed very grateful to the United States for their great effort in making these data available. . . . As you know, the activities of the World Meteorological Organization are to a large extent dependent on the efforts made by its Member States, and it is indeed a pleasure for me to express once again our sincere thanks to the United States for what it has done in the field of satellite meteorology, not only measured in dollars and personnel, but in initiative and enthusiasm which cannot fail to bring our science forward."

During 1962, the United States and Canada conducted an extensive program of TIROS IV—aircraft observations to investigate further the use of weather satellites for ice reconnaissance. This TIREC program is another example of international cooperation. During a discussion of the program (see Reference 13-6), Mr. T. A. Harwood, Canadian Defense Research Board, stated:

"Here are a series of meteorological satellites being sent up. The cost is literally fantastic. It is out of the pocketbook of the United States taxpayer, and in the case of the results which are going to take place in the Gulf of St. Lawrence over the next five years, . . . there will be a direct accrual to the Canadian economy which is, in a sense, in opposition to the United States economy. . . . This open-handedness—this availability of satellite photographs . . . is a direct gift to the Canadians of inestimable value. I think all the Canadians here will agree with this. . . . Of course, if things like this can go on elsewhere in the world, we'd like to think it would be a far better world to live in."

14

Outlook and Future Opportunities

Not all ideas for meteorological satellites come from senior engineers and scientists. During the spring of 1963, a group of college students designed a weather satellite system and, in the process, suggested some novel techniques not previously proposed by professional workers in this field.

Weather satellites are complex devices requiring many skills, including optics, structures, power, electronics, and others. The final design must be a compromise between the requirements of the many subsystems. No single subsystem can be designed alone; its design must be coordinated with the requirements and capabilities of the other subsystems. The sensors, for example, must not require more power, space, or weight than the power supply, satellite structure (including the needs of other subsystems) and launch vehicle make possible.

However, the amount of information needed to become proficient in even a single scientific or engineering specialty has caused college education to become compartmentalized. It seldom provides systems design experience in coordination, trade-offs, integration, and optimization. To overcome this deficiency, in the spring of 1963 the Massachusetts Institute of Technology offered an experimental interdepartmental course in systems engineering education. Its objective was (see Reference 14-1): "to give students experience in and an appreciation of the *over-all* problems involved in carrying out the preliminary design phase of a typical complex engineering system while at the same time permitting them to examine in considerable detail one particular aspect of the system." The students obtained practical experience in the types of tasks assigned so many engineers and scientists during projects such as TIROS, Nimbus, and many others which did not involve either meteorology or satellites. About 60 students, from such diverse courses as Electrical Engineering, Aeronautical and Astronautical Engineering, Industrial Management, Mechanical Engineering, Meteorology, and Civil Engineering took the course. As the course project, they designed an equatorial weather satellite system. So the course not only provided the desired systems engineering training; the participants designed an excellent meteorological satellite. The program and the satellite are discussed in the report: *MITROS, A Preliminary Design and Feasibility Study of an Equatorial Weather Satellite System* (see Reference 14-1).

Although the system included a launch vehicle and its supporting equipment, data processing, and communications, we will consider only the major aspects of the satellite, which would be equally usable in a quasi-polar orbit.

The MITROS satellite is shown in Figure 14-1. It is basically two cylinders, well separated but connected by a long semi-rigid boom. The boom is a metal tube, which is split along one side, flattened and coiled for launch; and then unrolled, reformed, and deployed in space. The lower package contains the sensors, a yaw attitude control gyro, and the various other electronics and communications equipment.

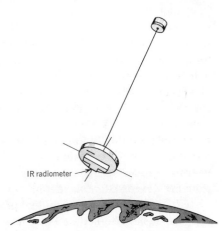

IR radiometer

Fig. 14-1. The MITROS satellite. (MIT)

The upper cylinder is the power source, a SNAP (Space Nuclear Auxiliary Power) nuclear generator. It is separated from the lower instruments package to avoid heavy shielding, otherwise required to prevent nuclear radiation from deteriorating the instruments and electronic components. In the SNAP generator, nuclear disintegrations provide heat. Thermoelectric or thermionic materials, placed between this heat and the cold of outer space, generate current, just as thermocouples would, but more efficiently. Neither solar cells nor storage batteries are required. This type of power has been used on the TRANSIT (navigation) satellites, and for ground-based automatic weather stations in remote areas (see Reference 14-2). The plans for future Nimbus also include a SNAP power source (see Reference 11-G-1) when the Nimbus power needs exceed the limits of solar cells.

The package separation is also used for MITROS attitude control, in pitch and roll, using the gravity gradient principle. Because of the decrease of gravity with height, two connected but separated masses (such as a gymnastic dumbbell) will maintain an orientation such that their connecting axis is aligned along the vertical (see Reference 14-32).

To see why, assume in Figure 14-1 that the MITROS axis tips away from the vertical. We choose the center of mass of the total satellite (mid-way along the boom) as our reference fulcrum, or point of rotation. Because gravity decreases with height, about this fulcrum the instrument package is pulled toward the earth (the torque is greater) more than for the power package. The boom is turned back towards the vertical. Because of other forces, the equilibrium orientation is not quite vertical, but the departure can be calculated.

If MITROS should be upside down after launch (a possibility, since either orientation is in gravity gradient equilibrium), this would be apparent from the pictures. A ground controlled magnetic coil, similar to that in TIROS, would turn MITROS to approximately the right position; gravity gradient could then take over.

Gravity gradient stabilization has been proven using the TRANSIT spacecraft (see Reference 14-32). In fact, gravity gradient influences the attitude of any satellite, even TIROS, as discussed in Reference 5-3. But there remain uncertainties as regards:

(1) The time required to damp oscillations and attain stabilization (possibly as much as a month).

(2) Accuracy of final stabilization.

(3) Ability to counteract external disturbances, such as micrometeorite impacts.

(4) Ability to counteract internal rotations such as gyros, scanners, and the starting, stopping or changing speed of tape recorders.

Yaw attitude control for MITROS uses a gyro, with a star-tracker to correct for gyro drifts.

MITROS was designed as a direct-readout (APT-type) satellite, although recorders would be feasible if gravity gradient stabilization can cope with their rotations. The daytime cloud pictures would be taken by a slow-scan TV camera, but in an arrangement providing a single horizon-to-horizon scan line per frame (Figure 14-2), instead of the usual square-field-of-view frame. A horizon-to-horizon viewing fan of 10,000 fiber optics fibers (tiny "light-pipes") is "folded" at the vidicon to form a square pattern on the face of the tube. Each TV frame would cover the same field of view as one rotation of the Nimbus HRIR scanning mirror. The frame rate would be matched to the velocity of the satellite, with one frame for each advance equal to the width of the scan "line." This is one of the novel concepts suggested in the design of MITROS.

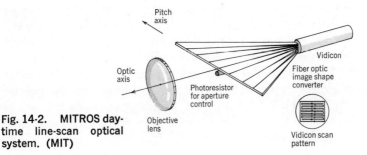

Fig. 14-2.   MITROS day-time line-scan optical system. (MIT)

A second is the night IR cloud sensor which is in most ways the same as the Nimbus HRIR subsystem. The two novel aspects are:

(1) The system uses horizon position information, from the radiometer, to determine satellite roll.

(2) The scanning mirror, using a pair of fixed mirrors, also views the fore and aft horizons to determine satellite pitch.

Weather satellites with features similar to those the students chose in their design of MITROS are being given serious consideration for operational purposes. If gravity gradient stabilization works satisfactorily, its lack of moving parts and need for power, and its consequent simplicity and presumed reliability, make it most attractive. Such configurations will be in active competition with the spin-stabilized Cartwheel design (Chapter 11) as a supplement to or a replacement for Nimbus. Much study and testing remains before the best of the possible configurations can be determined.

Neither TIROS, Nimbus, the Cartwheel, nor MITROS solve the problem of frequent observations and the timely detection of severe storms, except through the expedient of a large number of satellites in complementary orbits. At orbit altitudes below 4,000 miles, one satellite will see much of the earth only twice a day.

One method of obtaining the very frequent observations necessary to detect short-lived and often severe storms would be meteorological satellites in synchronous orbits (see Reference 14-31). As discussed in Chapter 12, the Synchronous Meteorological Satellite would be in a 22,300-mile orbit where, with its 24-hour period, it would appear to sit over a fixed point on the equator. Such a satellite, at 90° W (about over Galapagos Island), could constantly monitor the weather not only of the entire United States but all of Central America, South America, and southern portions of Canada.

The Synchronous Meteorological Satellite (SMS) has at times been referred to as Aeros. In Figure 14-3, its general configuration is "guesstimated" as similar to Nimbus. It would have many of the same types of subsystems as Nimbus, and at least one additional type:

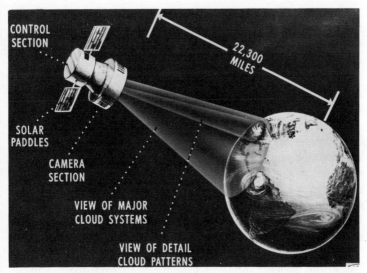

Fig. 14-3.   Synchronous meteorological satellite. (NASA)

(1) Power. This could be provided by solar paddles or a SNAP-type system.

(2) Controls. From this altitude, the diameter of the earth encompasses only some 20°, and 100 miles on the earth only about 0.25°. Accordingly, the controls system must be far more precise than for Nimbus if the cameras are to be aimed where desired, and if clouds are to be precisely located—a vital necessity for usefully observing small features. An improvement over Nimbus of 10 to 100 times would seem to be required. A star-tracking system may be necessary, since the opposite horizons are themselves only 20° apart.

(3) Station-keeping subsystem. This is the new one, not required on lower-orbiting satellites. At the 22,300-mile altitude, various disturbing factors (including the gravitational pull of the moon and the non-spherical shape of the earth) cause satellites to drift from stationary positions. To overcome these effects, small rocket motors or gas jets would be operated on ground command.

(4) Camera Subsystem. Two types of observations are

anticipated. The first would use a camera with resolution of the order of the TIROS camera or the Nimbus AVCS (1-3 miles) to survey the entire portion of the earth within view about once an hour. This might be a single picture, but more likely a series of pictures. Based on these data, and analysis of other meteorological observations, areas of greatest weather activity and interest would be determined—squall lines, severe thunderstorms, hurricanes, etc. These storms would then be frequently observed in detail with a high-resolution camera, commanded from the ground. Such data would be obtained at the rate of a picture every five to twenty minutes (for each critical area), covering a hundred to a few hundred miles on a side and with resolutions of perhaps 0.1 mile, so that individual clouds could be seen and identified. While both types of data might be obtained using a single camera with a "zoomar"-type or variable-focus telescopic lens, it is more likely that several different cameras with fixed-focus lens of different resolutions will be employed. This alternative is favored because of the complexity of the variable-focus lens, the lubrication problems its moving lens tube creates, and the partial redundancy provided by multiple cameras.

(5) Other sensors. Because of the distance from the earth, and the small amounts of infrared or radio energy reaching these levels from individual weather features, most other sensors contemplated for lower-level satellites are probably not feasible. Low resolution radiometers to measure large-scale albedos, emitted thermal radiation, and other earth-atmosphere heat balance parameters will probably be included, but the use of infrared sensors for night cloud observations, or to measure temperatures, presently seems beyond the state-of-the-art.

The synchronous meteorological satellite would have the usual other subsystems such as command, engineering telemetry, radio receivers, transmitters, antennas, etc. Other problem areas foreseen include:

(1) Radiation protection for electronic and optical components, since the satellite would be within the outer portion of the Van Allen belt.

(2) Temperature control, since the satellite would spend over 22 hours of each day in direct sunlight. Various portions of the satellite would spend consecutive periods of several hours with the sun shining directly on them, followed by periods of several hours of looking only at the cold of outer space.

The satellite would be controlled from a single master ground station, which also would serve as the primary data acquisition station. Several weather stations, within view of the spacecraft, also might be equipped to receive data in parallel with transmissions to the master station. This would eliminate delays in the reception of data on short-lived weather systems. Because the satellite would always be within view, data transmission rates could be relatively slow—perhaps a minute or so per picture as against the six seconds for Nimbus. Far smaller antennas may be adequate in spite of the greater distance between the satellite and the ground station.

A Synchronous Meteorological Satellite might double as a synchronous communications satellite, especially for the global distribution of data. In early 1964, Republic Aircraft completed, for NASA, initial design studies of a Synchronous Meteorological Satellite system.

One problem common to all meteorological satellites is that one-half of their time is spent over dark parts of the earth, where illumination is inadequate for the vidicon cameras. While infrared techniques can provide cloud cover data, usually in lesser detail, from low level orbits, infrared techniques do not appear feasible from synchronous altitudes. A TV camera able to operate at night would be desirable for meteorological satellites.

Image orthicon TV cameras (see Reference 5-7), able to work with only star-light illumination, have been developed. It remains to be proven whether such sensitive cameras can withstand the shocks and accelerations of launch. Even if they can, two other problems will remain.

(1) Certain gases in the high atmosphere, including oxygen and some of the oxides of nitrogen, faintly emit a glow in

certain parts of the visible spectrum. This "air-glow," as it is called, is similar to the Aurora (Northern Lights), although weaker and always present (see References 14-33, -34). At less than one-third of a full moon, the light from the air-glow is comparable to the starlight and moonlight reflected from clouds, and would seriously "fog" the cloud pictures. Either filters able to eliminate these air-glow bands (without reducing the other light) must be developed, or even an image orthicon camera will be useful, at night, only during two-thirds of each month.

(2) At dawn and dusk, illumination varies rapidly. Either the image-orthicon camera would need an extremely wide range of response, or properly positioned variable density filters must be developed. For the synchronous meteorological satellite, this will be a serious problem, since the dawn or dusk line will be within view over fifty per cent of the time.

For lower level orbits, night-time cloud observations might use high-resolution TV cameras operating in window regions (4, later 10, microns) of the infrared spectrum. These would provide data similar to that from Nimbus HRIR, or TIROS Channel 2 (8-12 micron window), but at high resolution. Development problems include the lower radiation energies at these wavelengths, and materials, sensitive to these wavelengths, usable in TV tubes.

Present meteorological satellite TV camera systems require one unit for observing and a separate tape recorder for storing the data. Magnetic tape is a rather inefficient way of recording picture data. In the TIROS vidicon, a picture on the sensitive surface occupies an area of less than 0.2 square inches; in the Nimbus AVCS, the area is nearly 0.5 square inches, but the resolution and amount of information stored is greater. A satellite cloud picture occupies about one square inch on 35-mm film. However, in both the TIROS and the Nimbus tape recorders, a single picture requires between 23 and 25 square inches, 25-50 times the area.

To overcome these problems, RCA is developing an Electrostatic Tape or Dielectric Tape camera (see Reference 14-3) in which a single tape, of materials similar to the sensitive elements in a TV vidicon, not only initially records the image, but also stores a series of such images until readout scan-off is commanded. The tape can be erased and reused many times. The Dielectric camera could replace both the vidicon camera and the tape recorder.

It is anticipated that the Dielectric Camera will be used in later Nimbus. At first, it may provide only one picture per orbit, of a 1500 × 1500 mile area at 0.1-mile resolution, for selected areas of greatest meteorological interest. Later, it should provide global coverage at a 0.2-mile resolution. It may ultimately replace the AVCS cameras, due to the greater resolution of its compact storage capability.

Another problem with present meteorological satellite recorders is that the tape is erased as soon as it has been readout. The data are then not directly available to more than a single CDA station. When meteorological satellite CDA stations are constructed outside North America, it would be desirable to be able to readout a tape two or more times, over different locations, before it was erased and used to record new data. This would reduce the need for intercontinental ground-to-ground communications for distribution of meteorological satellite data. NASA's Goddard Space Flight Center has developed a laboratory model of a 1200-foot endless-loop tape recorder with this "non-destructive"—or multiple—readout capability (see Reference 14-3), and is proceeding to the engineering of a flight model.

Turning now from the future of cloud pictures, infrared observations at several wavelengths may be used to measure the vertical distribution of temperature, moisture, or ozone in the atmosphere (see Chapter 6). The National Weather Satellite Center of the Weather Bureau and its contractor, Barnes Engineering Company, are developing an infrared spectrometer designed to measure the temperature at the surface (or the tops of the clouds) and in four layers of the atmosphere (see Reference 14-4). The instrument is intended for use in later Nimbus.

In this spectrometer, the infrared rays are focused on an optical diffraction grating. The grating, a series of very fine and precise lines, acts like a prism to divide the radiation into its spectral components. (Similar but cruder gratings are used in earrings and other jewelry to provide a twinkling rainbow appearance.) This avoids filters, which absorb energy and cannot as precisely separate spectral regions. The spectrum is then focused on five detectors, each precisely positioned to measure only its part of the grating-produced spectrum.

A laboratory model of this instrument has been constructed and tested. A second version has been tested from a high-level Skyhook-type balloon. Much work still remains to achieve size, weight, power requirements, ruggedness, and dependability vital to use in a satellite. Beyond this spectrometer will lie the development of others able to measure all the ten levels proposed by Kaplan (see Reference 6-2), rather than the mere four selected by Wark (see References 14-5, -6) for this simplified pioneering experiment. Still others will be required for observing water vapor, ozone, and possibly other atmospheric constituents. This will be a program continuing for many years and including theoretical studies, instrument designs and construction, data analysis, and meteorological and physical interpretation of the results. These will in turn lead to newer and better approaches and instruments of types which cannot even be foreseen as this is written.

Infrared and radio waves are merely arbitrary names for different wavelengths in the electromagnetic spectrum. There is no basic difference between longer infrared and shorter radio waves (microwaves); one part of the spectrum blends continuously into the next. As a corollary, just as the earth, clouds, and atmosphere emit infrared radiation, similar emissions (proportional to temperature) are produced in the microwave portion of the spectrum. The major differences between the emissions are:

(1) Emissions at microwave frequencies have less energy and vary more slowly with temperature than at infrared wavelengths.

(2) Instead of radiation detectors, sensitive microwave radio receivers similar to radar receivers are used. The sensi-

tivity and precise tuning of microwave receivers can compensate for the low power of the emitted energy (see Reference 14-6).

Because these observations require only a suitable radio receiver, compared to the transmitter-receiver combination of radar, they are called "passive microwave radiometry." They are attractive because:

(1) Several atmospheric gases, including oxygen and water, might be used to determine temperatures, perhaps more precisely than in the infrared.

(2) While clouds are opaque in the infrared, they are transparent in parts of the microwave region. Using passive microwaves, temperatures and other properties perhaps can be measured in and below clouds.

No specific meteorological satellite experiments in the passive microwave region have been designed, but a conference on this topic was held at RAND during 1962 (see Reference 14-35). There will be many future chances to contribute significantly to this novel field for, as Hanel and Wark state (see Reference 14-6):

"Before useful meteorological experiments can be performed in this spectral range, many physical parameters must be considered. Absorption coefficients of atmospheric gases, extinction cross-sections of water droplets and ice crystals, the transmissivity of clouds and the emissivity of various types of terrain, plus state of the art of low-noise receivers, are important design criteria."

Radar is a short wavelength radio signal, detected and measured when reflected from some object. When used for meteorological observation, raindrops, snowflakes, clouds, etc., provide the echoes (see Reference 14-7). In the radarscope, storms can be seen to form, grow, move, and dissipate.

In 1957, Touart and the author (see Reference 14-8) suggested the use of radar in meteorological satellites. The idea was expanded by Mook and Johnson (see Reference 14-9). In 1962, after several satellite weather radars had been designed in broad concept (see References 14-10, -11, -12), the author proposed a complementary study of the probable meteorological value of such data. Mr. Arnett S. Dennis conducted the study (see Reference 14-13). Dr. Morris Tepper, Director of Meteorological Systems, NASA, stated (see Reference 14-14):

"A recent study concluded by Stanford Research Institute shows, moreover, that even if the technological difficulties could be overcome, the meteorological usefulness (of a satellite radar) would be too limited to justify proceeding with such a development. We have put aside our flight experiment plans for a satellite radar."

Dennis's report (see Reference 14-13) provided three reasons for this conclusion:

(1) At the maximum detectability of a weather satellite radar, less than forty per cent of the precipitation would be observed.

(2) Viewed other than directly down, it would be difficult to distinguish an echo, from rain, from the very strong echo of the earth itself, because of the finite width of the radar beam.

(3) Nagle (see Reference 14-15), in a fundamental study comparing TIROS and radar data, has shown that radar rain patterns with large-scale or long-term significance are obtained only over a period of several hours. But a satellite can obtain only an instantaneous pattern, and it comes over too seldom to provide short-term data really useful to the local forecaster.

Accordingly, Dennis concludes (see Reference 14-13): "A meteorological satellite radar, assuming it were technically successful, would be an extremely complex means of acquiring crude estimates of the instantaneous rainfall rate, a rapidly fluctuating function which is only loosely correlated with the prevailing synoptic situation. Such data would be of negligible importance to weather forecasters dealing with either local or large-scale systems, and would be too crude to provide reliable inputs to research programs involving climatology or the general circulation."

Such failures of what initially appear to be sound concepts are common in science, and are fundamental to its progress;

each failure is one thing that does not work, and tells us to look elsewhere. Yet, some day a new electronic or meteorological discovery may overcome the limitations that led to Dennis' conclusions, as sound as they presently are. This, too, is the way of scientific progress.

Another possible radio observation from satellites is *sferics*. Sferics are radio signals generated in rain clouds, in association with lightning; they can locate storms and perhaps estimate their severity (see Reference 14-16). The radio static during a summer thunderstorm is sferics.

If the direction of a sferic could be measured at a satellite, it would determine which cloud-covered areas are associated with significant storminess. Even an omni-directional, purely stroke-counting detector, comparable to the Suomi radiometer, would provide research data on the global distribution of thunderstorms.

A sferics detector would require only a radio receiver and recorder. One problem will be accurate determination of the direction of the signals. Although sferics signals are maximum at low frequencies (about 10 Kc) and have decreasing strength as frequency increases, studies in England (by Horner) and by IBM (Hallgren and MacDonald) have indicated there is adequate signal strength at the shorter wavelengths to penetrate the ionosphere and be detected by the satellite.

In April 1962, the National Weather Satellite Center convened a conference of experts to discuss sferics measurements from satellites (see Reference 14-17). The British are considering an omni-directional sferics counter for one of their satellites, built and launched with the cooperation of NASA, of which Ariel was the first.

As the author has pointed out (see Reference 14-18), although present and future "capabilities are impressive, meteorological satellites . . . have very distinct and significant limitations. In particular, there are no ways presently foreseeable to make measurements, with useful accuracy, of the dynamic and static parameters most commonly employed in primary existing forecasting techniques—such as pressure, wind direction or velocity, and detailed vertical distributions of temperature in the free atmosphere. Nor can these be adequately inferred from data the satellites reap so well." These limitations are shown in Figure 3-3. The accuracy necessary to determine the velocity of a cloud, and so the wind velocity, from a satellite, in lower level orbits, may be too stringent for practical application (see References 14-8, -19). From a synchronous meteorological satellite, or one orbiting near 1500 nautical miles, cloud velocity measurements may be feasible if satellite attitude is accurately known, or if adequate landmarks are visible.

There are, however, recent developments that may cause the author to regret those words.

Jones, Fischbach, and Peterson of the University of Michigan (see Reference 14-20) have proposed measuring atmospheric densities and pressures by observing the refraction of light rays, from stars near the horizon, as they pass through the atmosphere to the satellite. When light passes through media of varying density, the rays are bent. A common example is the apparent bending of a spoon in a glass of water. Due to this effect, the sun is actually below the horizon before it appears to have set.

A satellite might measure the apparent changes in position, relative to their astronomical positions, of rising stars towards which it is moving, and of setting stars. From several observations of the variations in the refraction of light, the variations with altitude of atmospheric density can be calculated. Once a profile of densities was determined, it could be converted to the distribution in altitude of temperature and pressure.

The method depends on satellite stability, star tracker accuracies, and the validity of certain assumptions. Even if it will work, it is unlikely to give information below 15,000 feet, due to the interference of clouds.

The laser (see References 14-21, -22) might also be used for satellite measurements of atmospheric densities, pressure, temperatures, and winds. A laser (an acronym for Light Amplification by the Stimulated Emission of Radiation) can generate extremely intense light. Light from a laser has the following special properties:

(1) An extremely narrow beam.

(2) The light is monochromatic; that is, all at a single wavelength;

(3) The electromagnetic light waves are in phase, as for a radio transmission. This property, coherence, is far different than for other light sources, where the phases of the light waves are randomly distributed. Coherent light is like a military band, in step; while normal light is like an unorganized crowd with few people in step.

(4) Because of coherence, laser emissions can provide a "light radar" (LIDAR), and can be modulated, like radio waves, to transmit great amounts of information.

Lasers require special substances contained in tubes whose length is "tuned" to the wavelength of radiation emitted by the substance. An intense pulse of radiation is built up in the tube, enough to leak through the less reflective end and produce the strong, monochromatic, and coherent laser light.

A LIDAR could throw light on a cloud below a satellite. Measuring the time for the laser pulse to travel to the cloud and back would determine the distance to the cloud. If the satellite height was known, the height of the cloud top could be determined. Precise satellite altitude could be obtained from orbit calculations and laser measurements over the ocean.

A second application would be atmospheric densities, temperatures, and pressures. Even clear air will scatter back a bit of light, and the amount will be proportional to the air density. This technique was used, using searchlights on the ground, to obtain some of the first measurements of high altitude air densities. With the intense beam of a laser, it could be detectable from a satellite. The reflected light intensities, and so the densities, could be determined at various altitudes; altitudes would be determined by the LIDAR technique.

A third application might be winds, using the doppler principle. The wavelength of radiation emitted, reflected, or received by a moving object is changed slightly, proportionate to the velocity parallel to the direction of the ray; just as the frequency (pitch) of a train horn increases when approaching, and decreases when the train is moving away.

Assume that a laser beam is looking at the atmosphere at an angle, rather than straight down. If there were winds toward or away from the satellite, the frequency of the reflected radiation would be altered in proportion to the wind speed, according to the doppler principle. Of course, the doppler shift due to the satellite's own velocity would be considered. Such a measurement may be possible only because of the monochromatic (single frequency) and coherent (common phasing) nature of the laser light. Similar doppler-shift laser techniques might be applied to the reflections from clouds.

None of these equipments have yet been built. Still other applications of lasers will be made in the future.

Stellar refraction and laser methods will be difficult because of the need for sophisticated equipment, precise measurements, and complex calculations. Another method is more immediately feasible.

All meteorological satellite techniques discussed so far are dependent on observations *at a distance* through detection at the satellite of electromagnetic radiative emissions or reflections from the atmosphere. Since the satellite is above the atmosphere, it cannot make ambient (direct-contact) measurements as do most conventional meteorological techniques.

This handicap can be overcome if global weather satellites are coordinated with ambient sensors in the atmosphere. Meteorological instruments in automatic stations (including ocean buoys) and on floating balloons would make the measurements; as a satellite passed over, it would interrogate them and they would radio it their observations. The satellite would store the data for telemetry to a CDA station. Such a system was one of the key recommendations of the CIPASH report (see Reference 13-G-8).

Mook and Johnson (see Reference 14-9) first suggested this concept, a radar-beacon transponder system interrogating automatic stations, as one application of a satellite radar. Later, Lally (see Reference 14-23) proposed that satellites track and position constant level balloons to obtain winds over all parts of the world, especially the data-sparse oceans. In 1961-62, the author was chairman of an interagency committee which first intensively studied the data collection satellite, especially as it would apply to tracking balloons for winds and to the location of crashed aircraft (see Reference 14-24). In 1963, Moody and the author (see Reference 14-18) discussed the enlarged uses of such a system: tracking of balloons; location of crashed aircraft; collection of data from automatic weather, oceanographic, seismic, geomagnetic, tsunami (tidal waves), and other geophysical observatories; location of returned space capsules; and possibly tracking of icebergs and even bird migrations (see Reference 14-28). These uses are illustrated in Figure 14-4.

The way such a system would work is shown in Figure 14-5. The satellite equipment (if Nimbus is used, it will require only ten per cent of its capabilities) would include a transmitter, antennas, receiver, and magnetic tape storage. The transmitter would send discrete address signals, with a brief reception period between each transmission. Each observing station within range would respond, but only to its address to prevent interference between nearby stations, with signals from which its range and data could be deduced. The satellite would be within range long enough for each station to respond to several successive transmission cycles. From the ranges between the station and the satellite, the position of the station can be calculated. The range and the observed data would be recorded in the satellite, along with a time signal which can, from orbital data, provide the location of the satellite at each interrogation. When the satellite passed over a data acquisition station, the tape would be read out. Processing of the observational data, and of the range data to determine the positions of drifting stations, would be done on the ground.

The key problem is accurate position location. Direction intersections, the normal Radio Direction Finding procedure, would require accurate directional antennas. Mr. David Cubbage of the Naval Research Laboratory proposed a far preferable procedure, using range intersections (see Reference 14-25).

Each observing station would need a receiver, an address

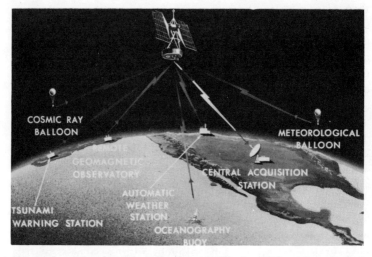

Fig. 14-4. Use of a data collection satellite to obtain meteorological and geophysical observations. (NASA)

Fig. 14-5. Diagram showing a data collection satellite system and the flow of the data. (JMSAC)

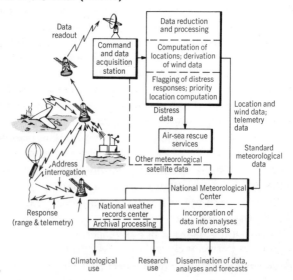

recognizer, a radio transmitter, the desired sensors, and power supplies. A most intriguing type of station would be a global array of hundreds of balloons, floating at constant levels in the atmosphere. These balloons would provide wind data, especially over data sparse ocean areas where this is probably the only feasible method. Each balloon would float for many days at a constant pressure level. The balloon and its electronics would be so light and brittle they would shatter on the slightest impact, creating no dangers in the unlikely event of an aircraft collision.

The Data Collection Satellite, especially with the global array of floating balloons, may constitute the next revolutionary development in meteorological observations.

Foreseeable observational techniques will create the problem of handling and transmitting tremendous quantities of data, even if only part of the systems we have discussed are implemented.

A great deal of meteorological data is redundant, but there is no way to eliminate redundancy until the data are analyzed. The redundancy in the cloud pictures, and the problems of its elimination, are particularly great. Ideally, the redundant information would be removed by automatic processing, on-board the satellite. One approach to this problem was proposed by Glaser (see Reference 14-26) in 1957, but no practical way to implement it, without destroying useful information, has yet been developed.

A single simple example (see Reference 14-27) illustrates the problem. Areas of cloud streets (parallel rows of cumulus clouds) often cover hundreds of square miles. Transmission of picture data at resolutions adequate to recognize these clouds demands radio bandwidths of hundreds of kilocycles. Yet all the meteorologists desire is the following information:

(1) Type of cloud (cumulus);
(2) Typical sizes of clouds;
(3) Type of pattern (cloud streets);
(4) Orientation (direction) of pattern;
(5) Distances between clouds and rows; and
(6) Area covered by this cloud pattern.

This information, if deduced in the satellite using automatic "On-Board Analysis," could far more easily be transmitted.

Cloud streets are a very simple pattern compared to many of the others in the satellite pictures. Any On-Board Analysis must, of course, be able to cope with all cloud patterns. But data beyond that providing useful information are redundant, wasteful of communications, and a burden to the analyst. If the analysis could be performed in the satellite, it would be of advantage to do so. If not, similar automatic analysis on the ground would aid the meteorologist, and the distribution of meteorological satellite data. The opportunities for contributions in this field of data compression are unlimited, and are apt to remain so for the foreseeable future. Openings for ingenious scientists, trained for research on these topics, will be plentiful for many years to come.

Another field without limitations to foreseeable opportunities is interpretation of the data already in existence and to be anticipated in the future. The use of satellite data in fundamental meteorological research, and in the development of improved techniques of weather analysis and forecasting, has only begun.

In many respects, it is not even clear which are the best ways to achieve these ends. As Touart and the author (see Reference 14-8) stated in 1957, and the situation is still not much different (see Reference 14-14):

"Present-day forecasting techniques and the data to be expected from a satellite are not (directly) compatible. The primary factors a forecaster uses in his business are the four-dimensional fields of motion, pressure, and temperature. While it is hoped the satellite will be able to gather . . . data of these types through the use of radiometers, at best they will be (somewhat) inferior . . . to our present day domestic observations . . .

"This leads to two possible avenues of attack: to tailor the satellite data to the forecaster or to tailor the forecaster to the data. The former seems the surer path. It means the primary objective is not to devise true forecasting techniques based on satellite data; instead, it involves means of translating satellite data into the kinds of information that are important to present day techniques. However, this does not imply complete disregard of the alternative . . . consideration should be given to the possibility that this new viewpoint will lead to fundamental changes in our understanding of the atmosphere and, may, therefore, lead to radically different forecasting techniques."

The many problems that remain include:

(1) How best to integrate radiation and cloud data into numerical weather prediction, which now uses principally pressure, temperature, and wind data? (see Reference 9-55).

(2) What is the value of the radiation data to long range forecasting? How best can this potential be achieved?

(3) Of the various radiation and cloud features, which ones are really significant sources of information? The answers are, of course, vital to any "On-Board Analysis."

(4) What is the significance of the spiral cloud patterns associated with major storms (see Reference 14-36)?

(5) Can wind velocity be inferred from cloud patterns, and with what accuracy?

(6) How do the heat gains and losses of the atmosphere, as observed from satellites, influence weather phenomena?

(7) How can the satellite data best be applied to climatology and to longer term changes in weather?

(8) What are the relationships between global cloud patterns and the subsequent state of the general circulation?

(9) What detail is needed in satellite observations to satisfy the needs of research workers and forecasters?

(10) What are the causes and significance of smaller scale cloud patterns, cells, and eddies, the existence of which first became known from TIROS pictures?

(11) Why are calculated and observed radiation values different in some wavelengths? Are there errors in the satellite sensors, or unknown absorbing layers in the atmosphere?

Any discussion of the future of meteorology, and especially of basic understanding of the atmosphere, leads inevitably to the question of weather modification; whether ultimately man can control his weather and climate. The problem is far too complicated to be properly discussed here. One of the better discussions is that of Greenfield, et al. (see Reference 14-29).

It is, however, important to point out, as Greenfield and his colleagues do, that:

"Meteorologists today have only a rudimentary and fragmentary knowledge of how energy fluctuates among the various scales of atmospheric motion and how these scaled phenomena modify and interact with one another. Any attempted modification of the weather, consisting as it does of a tampering with atmospheric interactions, may produce an unsuspected, uncontrollable, irreversible, or deleterious effect on the environment . . . such a result is only a remote possibility . . . however, the danger exists and increases in probability as the effective size of the area of modification approaches a considerable fraction of the surface area of the earth. It is evident that any tampering with natural phenomena is potentially dangerously to some degree and this danger can be minimized only by understanding the phenomena themselves and their reactions to the artificially induced effects."

The dangers of large scale weather control experiments, before we can reliably forecast their full consequences, have been well expressed in a WMO Report (see Reference 13-G-3):

"Modification of Weather and Climate"

"1. From current and contemplated research programmes, aided by satellites and other observational techniques, it is reasonable to expect a better knowledge of the general circulation and the heat balance of the atmosphere which in turn will lead to an improvement in our understanding of weather and climate.

"2. Indeed, it is not unrealistic to expect that mankind will eventually have the power to influence weather and even climate on a large scale; for example the artificial melting of the Arctic ice cap has been proposed. It is, however, imperative that the consequences of any such large-scale interference with the existing climatic balance should be accurately foreseen and evaluated.

"3. The complexity of atmospheric processes is such that an artificially induced change in the weather in one part of the earth will necessarily have repercussions in other parts. This principle can be affirmed on the basis of our present knowledge of the mechanism of the general circulation of the atmosphere. Our knowledge, however, is still very far from enabling us to forecast with confidence the degree, nature, or duration of the secondary effects to which a change in weather or climate in one part of the globe may give rise, nor even to predict whether these effects may be beneficial or detrimental.

"4. It must furthermore be borne in mind that a change of climate, even if regarded as beneficial, would necessarily lead to ecological changes in plant and animal life, whose consequences would be felt not only in the agriculture but in the whole economic and social life of the region concerned.

"5. Therefore, before starting an experiment on large-scale weather modifications, we must be sure of our capability of forecasting accurately the expected modification in the heat balance and the circulation of the atmosphere. Otherwise we could face some day the dangerous situation of undesired irreversible weather and climate changes.

"6. Consciously or not, man is engaged in a large-scale contamination of the earth's atmosphere which is bound to become more serious. We refer not only to contamination of the lower atmosphere by carbon dioxide and other gases, particulates, etc., which may have a significant effect on the earth's radiational balance, but also to the increasing contamination of the upper atmosphere."

Meteorological satellites will play two roles in whatever is the future of weather control:

(1) Providing research data necessary to the improved knowledge of the atmosphere, without which weather control would not be prudent—nor perhaps even possible.

(2) Providing parts of the global weather data necessary to

determine whether, at any given time, a proposed weather control operation is feasible and desirable.

It is not presently clear whether satellites may play an active role, in contrast to an observational service, in weather control. Few of the techniques so far proposed as possible ways of modifying the weather would involve a satellite. But science often leads to the unexpected.

The future of meteorology now extends beyond our own atmosphere. As the other planets become attainable, the meteorologist must apply his talents to understanding and forecasting weather conditions on Mars and Venus, and later for Jupiter and beyond. He must be prepared to deal with different combinations of gases, rates of planetary rotations, values of gravity, and solar heating rates than those of the earth. Our limited knowledge of these problems have been discussed by Kellogg and Sagan (see Reference 14-30).

The experience gained with earth-orbiting weather satellites will be invaluable as we prepare to explore other planets and their atmospheres. All we know about these atmospheres comes from measurements of visible, infrared, and microwave radiations. The Mariner II microwave radiometer, which confirmed the high Venus surface temperature, was much like those being considered for later weather satellites. The Mariner II infrared radiometer, which observed the Venus clouds, operated in the infrared window also used by TIROS.

The opportunities here have been well expressed by Kellogg and Sagan (see Reference 14-30):

"There have been organisms on our planet for about four thousand million years. By a remarkable stroke of fortune, it is in the next few decades that Man will first discover— rigorously, and in detail—what is happening on the neighboring worlds. The probability of our being alive at the present time, taken on a random basis, is therefore about a millionth of a percent. We are immensely lucky to be living at the dawn of this era of planetary exploration and high scientific adventure."

Similar thoughts apply to the new views of our own atmosphere provided by TIROS, Nimbus, and their successors.

References and Bibliography

This extensive list of References and Bibliography is provided for two purposes:

To give credit, in the manner traditional in all scientific fields, to those who have conducted the studies and developments that have made satellite meteorology what it is today.

To provide a ready list of source material for those readers who may wish to investigate more extensively one or more of the topics discussed in this book.

Those interested in studying some of these references may be able to consult or obtain many of them in one of the following places or organizations:

(1) Local stations of the U. S. Weather Bureau, of the Air Force's Air Weather Service, or of the Navy's Weather Service.

(2) University meteorology departments and libraries.

(3) Headquarters, NASA, Office of Scientific and Technical Information, Washington 25, D. C. (especially for NASA Reports and reprints of papers by NASA authors).

(4) National Weather Satellite Center, U. S. Weather Bureau, Washington, D. C. 20234 (especially for USWB Reports and reprints of papers by Weather Bureau authors).

(5) Superintendent of Documents, U. S. Government Printing Office, Washington, D. C. 20402 (for purchase of U. S. Government reports).

(6) American Meteorological Society, 45 Beacon Street, Boston 02108, Mass. (regarding copies of or material published in:

Bulletin of the American Meteorological Society
Weatherwise
Meteorological and Geoastrophysical Abstracts
Journal of Meteorology
Journal of Applied Meteorology
Journal of the Atmospheric Sciences)

These references and bibliographic sources are organized with first a General section listing material with rather broad and general coverage of the field of satellite meteorology. Then, for each chapter, are given general references (where there are applicable ones) followed by specific references to topics as discussed or cited in the text.

General References

G-1   American Rocket Society, 1960: Special Section on TIROS I, *Astronautics,* June 1960.

G-2   Goddard Space Flight Center, 1962: *Final Report on the TIROS I Meteorological Satellite System,* Technical Report R-131, NASA.

G-3   Jacobs, W. C., 1962: *Meteorological Satellites,* Staff Report for the Committee on Aeronautical and Space Sciences, U. S. Senate, U. S. Government Printing Office ($0.55).

G-4   Johnson, D. C. (USWB), 1962: "Meteorological Measurements from Satellites," *Bulletin of the American Meteorological Society,* Vol. 43, No. 9, pp. 481-484.

G-5   Kiss, E., (AMS), 1960: "Bibliography on the Use of Satellites in Meteorology," *Meteorological and Geoastrophysical Abstracts,* Vol. 11, No. 10, pp. 1683-1729.

G-6   Kiss, E., (AMS), 1963: "Supplementary Bibliography on the Use of Satellites in Meteorology," *Meteorological and Geoastrophysical Abstracts,* Vol. 14, No. 3, pp. 870-936. (also Vol. 15)

G-6A   Kiss, E., 1963: *Bibliography on Meteorological Satellites (1952-1962),* U. S. Department of Commerce, Weather Bureau, U. S. Government Printing Office ($1.25).

G-7   NASA and USWB, 1961: *Reprints of Reference Papers* for the International Meteorological Satellite Workshop.

G-8   NASA and USWB, 1961: *Proceedings of the International Meteorological Satellite Workshop,* U. S. Government Printing Office ($1.75).

G-9   Neiburger, M., (UCLA), and H. Wexler (USWB), 1961: "Weather Satellites," *Scientific American,* Vol. 205, No. 1, pp. 80-94.

G-10   Tepper, M. (NASA), 1961: "A Report on the Meteorological Satellite Program," *Weatherwise,* Vol. 14, No. 4, pp. 131-137, 168.

G-11   Tepper, M. (NASA), S. F. Singer (USWB), and J. Newbauer (Editors), 1963: Weather Satellite Systems issue, *Astronautics and Aerospace Engineering,* Vol. 1, No. 3.

G-12   U. S. Congress, House of Representatives Committee on Science and Astronautics, 1961: *National Meteorological Satellite Program* (Hearings before the Committee with several reprinted reports), U. S. Government Printing Office.

G-13   Valovcin, F., (Editor), 1961: *Contributions to Satellite Meteorology,* GRD Research Notes No. 36, Vol. II, Air Force Cambridge Research Laboratories.

G-14   Wexler, H. (USWB), 1961: "Meteorology," *Science in Space* (L. V. Berkner and H. Odishaw, Editors), McGraw-Hill, New York, pp. 139-155.

G-15   Wexler, H. and J. E. Caskey, Jr. (Editors), (USWB), 1963: *Proceedings of the International Symposium on Rocket and Satellite Meteorology*, April 1962, North-Holland Publishing Company, Amsterdam.

G-16   Wexler, H., and D. Johnson (USWB), 1961: "Meteorological Satellites," *Bulletin of the Atomic Scientists*, Vol. 17, No. 5/6, pp. 185-190.

G-17   Widger, W. K., Jr. (Editor), 1960: *Contributions to Satellite Meteorology*, GRD Research Notes No. 36, Air Force Cambridge Research Center.

G-18   Widger, W. K., Jr., 1960: *Examples of Project TIROS Data and Their Practical Meteorological Use*, GRD Research Notes No. 38, Air Force Cambridge Research Laboratories.

G-19   Widger, W. K., Jr., and C. N. Touart, 1957: "Utilization of Satellite Observations in Weather Analysis and Forecasting," *Bulletin of the American Meteorological Society*, Vol. 38, No. 9, pp. 521-533.

G-20   Lehr, P. E. (Editor), 1963: *Reduction and Use of Data Obtained by TIROS Meteorological Satellites* (Prepared by the National Weather Satellite Center of the United States Weather Bureau at the request of the WMO Executive Committee Panel of Experts on Artificial Satellites), Technical Note No. 49, World Meteorological Organization, Geneva, Switzerland.

G-21   Widger, W. K., Jr., P. E. Sherr, and C. W. C. Rogers, 1964: *Practical Interpretation of Meteorological Satellite Data*, Final Report, Contract No. AF 19(628)-2471, ARACON Geophysics Company. (Air Weather Service Technical Report 185)

CHAPTER 1

General

1-G-1   Wexler, H., and S. Fritz (both USWB), 1961: "Planet Earth as Seen from Space," *The Solar System, Vol. III: Planets and Satellites*, University of Chicago Press, pp. 1-11.

See Also *General References* G-2, G-8, G-15, G-18.

Specific

1-1   Fritz, S. (USWB), 1961: "Satellite Cloud Pictures of a Cyclone over the Atlantic Ocean," *Quarterly Journal of the Royal Meteorological Society*, Vol. 87, No. 373, pp. 314-321.

1-2   Bristor, C. L., and M. A. Ruzecki (both USWB), 1960: "TIROS I Photographs of the Midwest Storm of April 1, 1960," *Monthly Weather Review*, Vol. 88, No. 9/12, pp. 315-326.

1-3   Whitney, L. F., Jr., and S. Fritz (both USWB), 1961: "Tornado Producing Cloud Pattern Seen by TIROS I," *Bulletin of the American Meteorological Society,* Vol. 42, No. 9, pp. 603-614.

1-4   Hubert, L., and A. F. Krueger (USWB), 1962: "Satellite Pictures of Mesoscale Eddies," *Monthly Weather Review,* Vol. 90, No. 12, pp. 457-463.

1-5   Oliver, V. J. (USWB), 1960: "TIROS Pictures A Pacific Frontal Storm," *Weatherwise,* Vol. 13, No. 5, p. 186.

1-6   Serebreny, S. M., E. J. Wiegman, and R. G. Hadfield, 1962: *Investigation of the Operational Use of Cloud Photographs from Weather Satellites in the North Pacific,* Final Report under Contract No. Cwb 10238, Stanford Research Institute, Menlo Park, California.

CHAPTER 2

General

2-G-1   Lehr, P. E., W. Burnett, and H. S. Zim, 1957: *Weather,* Golden Press, No. 407, Simon and Schuster, New York ($1.00).

2-G-2   Battan, L. J., 1961: *The Nature of Violent Storms,* Anchor No. 519, Doubleday & Co., New York ($.95).

2-G-3   Forrester, F., 1957: *1001 Questions Answered About the Weather,* G & D No. 0805, Grosset & Dunlap, New York, ($2.45).

2-G-4   Loesbach, T., 1961: *Our Atmosphere,* Mentor, No. MD309, New York ($.50).

2-G-5   Longstreth, T. M., 1962: *Understanding the Weather,* Collier, No. AS321, New York.

2-G-6   Sutton, O. G., 1960: *Understanding Weather,* Pelican, No. A469, Penguin Books, Baltimore, Md., ($.95).

2-G-7   Spar, J., 1957: *The Way of the Weather,* Creative ($7.75).

2-G-8   Civil Aeronautics Administration, 1954: *Pilots' Weather Handbook,* CAA Technical Manual No. 104, U. S. Government Printing Office ($1.25).

2-G-9   Neuberger, H. H., and F. B. Stephens, 1948: *Weather and Man,* Prentice-Hall, New York.

2-G-10   Petterssen, S., 1941: *Introduction to Meteorology,* Mc-Graw-Hill, New York.

Specific

2-1   Cowen, R. C., 1964: "The Weather Computers," *The Nation,* Vol. 198, No. 4, pp. 71-73.

CHAPTER 3

Specific

3-1   Widger, W. K., Jr., 1963: "Meteorological Satellites and Weather Reconnaissance Aircraft—Complementary Observing

Systems," *Bulletin of the American Meteorological Society*, Vol. 44, No. 9, pp. 549-563.

3-2   Conover, J. H., 1962: *Cloud Interpretation from Satellite Altitudes*, AFCRL Research Note No. 81, Air Force Cambridge Research Laboratories (also included in G-15).

3-3   Erickson, C. O., and L. F. Hubert (both USWB), 1961: *Idenification of Cloudforms from TIROS I Pictures*, Meteorological Satellite Laboratory Report No. 7, USWB.

3-4   Lehr, P. E. (USWB), 1962: "Methods of Archiving, Retrieving, and Utilizing Data Acquired by TIROS Meteorological Satellites," *Bulletin of the American Meteorological Society*, Vol. 43, No. 10, pp. 539-548.

3-5   Widger, W. K., Jr., P. E. Sherr, and C. W. C. Rogers, 1964: *Practical Interpretation of Meteorological Satellite Data*, Final Report, Contract No. AF 19(628)-2471, ARACON Geophysics Company. (Air Weather Service Technical Report 185)

CHAPTER 4

General

4-G-1   Peterssen, S., 1941: *Introduction to Meteorology*, McGraw-Hill, New York (See Chapter 15, "History," pp. 217-224).

4-G-2   Shaw, Sir N., 1942: "Meteorology in History," Vol. 1 of *Manual of Meteorology*, Cambridge University Press.

4-G-3   Goddard Space Flight Center, 1962: *Final Report on the TIROS I Meteorological Satellite System*, Technical Report R-131, NASA (see pp. 1-16).

4-G-4   Jacobs, W. C., 1962: *Meteorological Satellites*, Staff Report for the Committee on Aeronautical and Space Sciences, U. S. Senate, U. S. Government Printing Office (pp. 23-36).

Specific

4-1   Abbe, Truman, 1955: *Professor Abbe and the Isobars*, Vantage, New York.

4-2   Dornberger, W., 1952: *V-2* (Translated by J. Cleugh and G. Halliday, 1954), Viking Press and Ballantine Books, New York.

4-3   Crowson, D. L., 1949: "Cloud Observations from Rockets," *Bulletin of the American Meteorological Society*, Vol. 30, No. 1, pp. 17-22.

4-4   Greenfield, S. M., and W. W. Kellogg, 1960: *Inquiry into the Feasibility of Weather Reconnaissance from a Satellite Vehicle*, RAND Corporation Report No. R-365, August 1960 (Unclassified edition of RAND Report No. R-218, issued 1951).

4-5   Wexler, H. (USWB), 1954: "Observing the Weather from a

Satellite Vehicle," *Journal of the British Interplanetary Society,* Vol. 13, pp. 269-276.

4-6   Hubert, L. F. (USWB), and O. Berg, 1955: "A Rocket Portrait of a Tropical Storm," *Monthly Weather Review,* Vol. 83, No. 6, pp. 119-124.

4-7   Wexler, H. (USWB), 1957: "The Satellite and Meteorology," *Journal of Astronautics,* Vol. 4, No. 1, pp. 5, 8.

4-8   Widger, W. K., Jr., 1961: "Satellite Meteorology—Fancy and Fact," *Weather,* Vol. 16, No. 2, pp. 47-55.

4-9   Singer, S. F., 1957: "Meteorological Measurements from a Minimum Satellite Vehicle," *Transactions of the American Geophysical Union,* Vol. 38, No. 4, pp. 469-482.

4-10   Weinstein, M., and V. E. Suomi, 1961: "Meteorological Applications of Explorer VII Infrared Radiation Measurements," *Transactions of the American Geophysical Union,* Vol. 42, No. 4, pp. 492-498.

4-11   Widger, W. K., Jr., and C. N. Touart, 1957: "Utilization of Satellite Observations in Weather Analysis and Forecasting," *Bulletin of the American Meteorological Society,* Vol. 38, No. 9, pp. 521-533.

4-12   Glaser, A. H., 1957: *Meteorological Utilization of Images of the Earth's Surface Transmitted from a Satellite Vehicle,* Final Report, Phase II, Contract No. AF19(604)-1589, Blue Hill Meteorological Observatory, Harvard University.

4-13   Hubert, L. F. (USWB), 1960: *Analysis of Project Hugo Test Firing, Dec. 5, 1958,* USWB, MSL Report No. 2, August, 1960.

4-14   Conover, J. H., and J. C. Sadler (AFCRL), 1960: "Cloud Patterns as Seen From Altitudes of 250 to 850 Miles: Preliminary Results," *Bulletin of the American Meteorological Society,* Vol. 41, No. 6, pp. 291-297.

4-15   Sadler, J. C., 1962: *Utilization of Meteorological Satellite Cloud Data in Tropical Meteorology,* CRL Research Note, Air Force Cambridge Research Laboratories (also included in G-15).

CHAPTER 5

General

5-G-1   Goddard Space Flight Center, 1962: *Final Report on the TIROS I Meteorological Satellite System,* Technical Report R-131, NASA.

5-G-2   NASA and USWB, 1961: *Proceedings of the International Meteorological Satellite Workshop,* U. S. Government Printing Office ($1.75).

5-G-3   American Rocket Society, 1960: "Special Section on TIROS I," *Astronautics,* June issue.

5-G-4   Rados, R. M., 1963: "TIROS Achievements," *Astronautics and Aerospace Engineering,* Vol. 1, No. 3, pp. 28-29.

5-G-5   Powers, E. F., 1963: "TIROS Operations," *Astronautics and Aerospace Engineering,* Vol. 1, No. 3, pp. 29-31.

Specific

5-1   Osgood, C. C., 1960: "Structural Design of TIROS I," *Astronautics,* June issue, pp. 42-43, 90-91.

5-2   Perkel, H., 1960: "TIROS I Spin Stabilization," *Astronautics,* June issue, pp. 38-39, 106.

5-3   Bandeen, W. R. (NASA), and W. P. Manger (RCA), 1960: "Angular Motion of the Spin Axis of the TIROS I Meteorological Satellite Due to Magnetic and Gravitational Torques," *Journal of Geophysical Research,* Vol. 65, No. 9, pp. 2992-2995.

5-4   Conrath, B. J. (NASA), 1962: *Earth Scan Analog Signal Relationships in the TIROS Radiation Experiment and Their Application to the Problem of Horizon Sensing,* Technical Note D-1341, NASA.

5-5   Glaser, A. H. (Allied Research Assoc.), 1961: *TIROS Meteorology,* Final Report under Contract No. AF19(604)-5581, Allied Research Associates, Inc. (see Appendix A, especially p. 74).

5-6   Glaser, A. H. (Allied Research Assoc.), 1960: *A System for the Meteorological Operational Use of Satellite Television Observations,* First Semi-Annual Technical Summary Report, Contract No. AF 19(604)-5581, Allied Research Associates, Inc.

5-7   Fink, D. G., and D. M. Lutyens, 1960: *The Physics of Television,* Anchor Books Science Study Series, Doubleday & Co., Inc., Garden City, New York.

5-8   Goldberg, E. A. and V. D. Landon, 1960: "Key Equipment for TIROS I," *Astronautics,* June issue, pp. 36-37, 98-99.

5-9   Mesner, M. H., and J. R. Staniszewski, 1960: "Television Cameras for Space Exploration," *Astronautics,* May issue, pp. 36–37, 127-129.

5-10   Keigler, J. E., and C. B. Oakley, 1960: "The TIROS System on the Ground," *Astronautics,* June issue, pp. 44-45, 100-102.

CHAPTER 6

General

6-G-1   Bandeen, W. R., R. A. Hanel, V. Licht, R. A. Stampfl, and W. G. Stroud (all NASA), 1961: "Infrared and Reflected Solar Radiation Measurements from the TIROS II Meteorological Satellite," *Journal of Geophysical Research,* Vol. 66, No. 10, pp. 3169-3185 (also published as NASA Technical Note D-1096).

6-G-2   Nordberg, W., 1961: Physical Measurements and Data Processing," *Proceedings of the International Meteorological Satellite Workshop*, U. S. Government Printing Office, pp. 107-119.

6-G-3   Nordberg, W. (NASA), 1963: "Research with TIROS Radiation Measurements," *Astronautics and Aerospace Engineering*, Vol. 1, No. 3, pp. 76-83.

6-G-4   Davis, J. F., R. A. Hanel, R. A. Stampfl, M. G. Strange, and M. R. Townsend, 1962: *Telemetering Infrared Data from the TIROS Meteorological Satellites*, NASA Technical Note D-1293.

6-G-5   Hanel, R. A., 1962: *Radiometric Measurements from Satellites*, NASA Technical Note D-1463.

Specific

6-1   Hanel, R. A., 1961: "An Instrument to Measure the Solar Constant from a Satellite," *NASA*, Technical Note D-674.

6-2   Kaplan, L. D., 1959: "Inference of Atmospheric Structure from Remote Radiation Measurements," *Journal of Optical Society of America*, Vol. 49, pp. 1004-1007.

6-3   King, Jean I. F., 1961: "Deduction of Vertical Temperature Structure of a Planetary Atmosphere from a Satellite," *Planetary and Space Science*, Vol. 7, pp. 423-426.

6-4   Bandeen, W. R., B. J. Conrath, and R. A. Hanel, 1963: "Experimental Confirmation from the TIROS VII Meteorological Satellite of the Theoretically Calculated Radiance of the Earth Within the 15 Micron Band of Carbon Dioxide," *Journal of Atmospheric Sciences*, Vol. 20, No. 6, pp. 609-614.

CHAPTER 7

General

7-G-1   Lehr, P. (USWB), 1962: "Methods of Archiving, Retrieving, and Utilizing Data Acquired by TIROS Meteorological Satellites," *Bulletin of the American Meteorological Society*, Vol. 43, No. 10, pp. 539-548.

7-G-2   Glaser, A. H. (ARACON Geophysics), 1960: "A System for the Meteorological Use of Satellite Television Observations," *Contributions to Satellite Meteorology*, GRD Research Notes, No. 36, GRD, AFCRC, pp. 63-91, 205-258.

7-G-3   Glaser, A. H., 1961: *TIROS Meteorology*, Final Report under Contract No. AF 19(604)-5581, Allied Research Associates, Inc.

7-G-4   Jones, J. B., and L. E. Mace (both NWSC), 1963: "TIROS Meteorological Operations," *Astronautics and Aerospace Engineering*, Vol. 1, No. 3, pp. 32-36.

7-G-5   Hubert, L. F., 1961: *TIROS I: Camera Attitude Data, Analysis of Location Errors, and Derivation of Corrections for Calibration*, USWB Meteorological Satellite Laboratory Report No. 5.

7-G-6   Hubert, L. F., 1961: *Canadian Grids for TIROS I, Additional Orientation Data and Errata*, USWB, Supplement to MSL Report No. 5.

7-G-7   Hubert, L. F., 1962: *Documentation for TIROS III Television Data*, USWB Meteorological Satellite Laboratory Report No. 9.

7-G-8   Fujita, T. (Univ. of Chicago), 1963: *A Technique for Precise Analysis for Satellite Data; Volume I—Photogrammetry*, USWB Meteorological Satellite Laboratory Report No. 14.

7-G-9   Cronin, J. R., and L. W. Abreu, 1963: *A Modification of the Fujita Method for TIROS Photograph Rectification*, Scientific Report No. 1, Contract No. AF 19(628)-320, ARACON Geophysics Company.

7-G-10   Widger, W. K., Jr., 1960: *Examples of Project TIROS Data and Their Practical Meteorological Use*, GRD Research Notes No. 38, GRD, AFCRL.

7-G-11   Doolittle, R. C. (USNPIC), Miller, L. I., and Ruff, I. S. (USWB), 1962: "Geographic Location of Cloud Features," *Final Report on the TIROS I Meteorological Satellite System*, NASA Technical Report R-131, pp. 335-355.

7-G-12   Pyle, R. L. (USWB), 1961: "Archiving of TIROS Data," *Proceedings of the International Meteorological Satellite Workshop*, NASA-USWB, U. S. Government Printing Office, pp. 153-155.

7-G-13   Bristor, C. L., E. G. Albert, and J. B. Jones (NWSC), 1961: "Problems in Mapping Data from Meteorological Satellites," *Space Research II* (Proceedings of the Second International Space Science Symposium), North-Holland Publishing Company, Amsterdam.

7-G-14   Bandeen, W. R., 1962: "Data Processing from Meteorological Satellites," *Proceedings of the NASA-University Conference on the Science and Technology of Space Exploration*, Nov. 1-13, 1962.

7-G-15   Nordberg, W. (NASA), 1961: "Physical Measurements and Data Processing," *Proceedings of the International Meteorological Satellite Workshop*, NASA-USWB, U. S. Government Printing Office, Washington, D. C., pp. 107-119.

7-G-16   NASA GSFC, 1961: *TIROS II Radiation Data User's Manual*, NASA Goddard Space Flight Center.

7-G-17   Bandeen, W. R., 1962: *Supplement to TIROS II Radiation Data User's Manual*, NASA Goddard Space Flight Center.

7-G-18   NASA GSFC, 1962: *TIROS III Radiation Data User's Manual,* NASA Goddard Space Flight Center.

Specific

7-1   Pyle, R. L., and D. M. Mercer, 1961: *Catalogue of Meteorological Satellite Data: TIROS I Television Cloud Photography,* USWB, Keys to Meteorological Records Documentation No. 5. 31.

7-2   USWB, 1962: *Catalogue of Meteorological Satellite Data: TIROS III Television Cloud Photography,* Keys to Meteorological Records Documentation No. 5. 33.

7-3   NASA GSFC, 1961: *TIROS II Radiation Data Catalog,* NASA Goddard Space Flight Center.

7-4   NASA GSFC, 1963: *TIROS III Radiation Data Catalog,* NASA Goddard Space Flight Center.

CHAPTER 8

General

8-G-1   Mace, L. M. (USWB), and J. B. Jones (AWS), 1962: "Operational Assists by TIROS," *Weatherwise,* Vol. 15, No. 3, pp. 97-101.

8-G-2   Jones, J. B., and L. M. Mace, 1963: TIROS Meteorological Operations," *Astronautics and Aerospace Engineering,* Vol. 1, No. 3, pp. 32-36.

8-G-3   Winston, J. S. (USWB), 1961: "Use of TIROS Pictures in Current Synoptic Analysis," *Proceedings of the International Meteorological Satellite Workshop,* U. S. Government Printing Office, pp. 95-105.

8-G-4   Jacobs, W. C., 1962: *Meteorological Satellites,* Staff Report for the U. S. Senate Committee on Aeronautical & Space Sciences, U. S. Government Printing Office, pp. 66ff., 83ff.

8-G-5   Glaser, A. H., 1960: *TIROS I: An Operational Evaluation of a New Meteorological Tool,* Second Semi-Annual Technical Summary Report under Contract No. AF 19(604)-5581, Allied Research Associates, Inc.

8-G-6   Widger, W. K., Jr., 1960: "Examples of Project TIROS Data and Their Practical Meteorological Use," *GRD Research Notes No. 38,* Air Force Cambridge Research Laboratories.

8-G-7   Tepper, M. (NASA), 1961: "Summary of Operational Utilization of TIROS II Data," *1962 NASA Authorization Hearings* before the House of Representatives Committee on Science and Astronautics, U. S. Government Printing Office, pp. 412-419.

8-G-8   Tepper, M., 1962: "Meteorological Systems—Operational Value and Use of TIROS III Data," *1963 NASA Authorization Hearings* before the House of Representatives Subcommittee on

Applications and Tracking and Data Acquisition, U. S. Government Printing Office, pp. 2012-2016.

8-G-9   Johnson, D. S. (USWB), 1962: "Summary of Operational Use Made of TIROS III Picture Data," *1963 NASA Authorization Hearings* before the House of Representatives Subcommittee on Applications and Tracking and Data Acquisition, U. S. Government Printing Office, pp. 2174-2175.

Specific

8-1   Jones, J. B. (AWS), 1961: "A Western Atlantic Vortex as Seen by TIROS I," *Monthly Weather Review,* Vol. 89, No. 10, pp. 383-390.

CHAPTER 9

General

9-G-1   Wexler, H., and J. E. Caskey, Jr. (USWB), 1963: *Proceedings of the First International Symposium on Rocket and Satellite Meteorology,* North-Holland Publishing Company, Amsterdam.

9-G-2   Fritz, S. (USWB), 1963: "Meteorological Satellites in the United States," in "IUGG Triennial Report (USA)," *Transactions of the American Geophysical Union,* Vol. 44, No. 2, pp. 406-410.

9-G-3   Fritz, S., 1963: "Research with Satellite Cloud Pictures." *Astronautics and Aerospace Engineering,* Vol. 1, No. 3, pp. 70-74.

9-G-4   Nordberg, W. (NASA), 1963: "Research with TIROS Radiation Measurements," *Astronautics and Aerospace Engineering,* Vol. 1, No. 3, pp. 76-83.

9-G-5   NASA and USWB, 1961: *Proceedings of the International Meteorological Satellite Workshop,* U. S. Government Printing Office.

9-G-6   Widger, W. K., Jr., P. E. Sherr and C. W. C. Rogers, 1964: *Practical Interpretation of Meteorological Satellite Data,* Final Report, Contract No. AF 19(628)-2471, ARACON Geophysics Company. (Air Weather Service Technical Report 185)

Specific

9-1   Fitz Roy, R., 1863: *The Weather Book. A Manual of Practical Meteorology,* 2nd Ed., Longman, Green, Longman, Roberts, and Green, London.

9-2   Boucher, R. J., and R. J. Newcomb (ARACON Geophysics) 1962: "Synoptic Interpretation of Some TIROS Vortex Patterns: A Preliminary Cyclone Model," *J. Applied Meteorology,* Vol. 1, No. 2, pp. 127-136.

9-3   Bristor, C. L., and M. A. Ruzecki (USWB), 1960: "TIROS I Photographs of the Midwest Storm of April 1, 1960," *Monthly Weather Review,* Vol. 88, No. 9-12, pp. 315-324.

9-4   Fritz, S. (USWB), 1961: "Satellite Cloud Pictures of a Cyclone over the Atlantic Ocean," *Quarterly Journal of the Royal Meteorological Society,* Vol. 87, No. 373, pp. 314-321.

9-5   Winston, J. S., and L. Tourville (USWB), 1961: "Cloud Structure of an Occluded Cyclone over the Gulf of Alaska as Viewed by TIROS I," *Bulletin of the American Meteorological Society,* Vol. 42, No. 3, pp. 151-165.

9-6   Winston, J. S. (USWB), 1960: "Satellite Pictures of a Cut-off Cyclone over the Eastern Pacific," *Monthly Weather Review,* Vol. 88, No. 9-12, pp. 295-314.

9-7   Bjerknes, J., and H. Solberg, 1922: "Life Cycle of Cyclones and Polar Front Theory of Atmospheric Circulation," *Geophysics Publication,* Vol. 3, No. 1.

9-8   Merritt, E., 1963: *Fleet Applications, Meteorological Operational Satellites (Antarctic Area),* Final Report, Contract No. N 189(188)-56507A, ARACON Geophysics Company.

9-9   Nagle, R. E., and S. M. Serebreny (SRI), 1962: "Radar Precipitation Echo and Satellite Cloud Observations of a Maritime Cyclone," *Journal of Applied Meteorology,* Vol. 1, No. 3, pp. 279-295.

9-10   Kreuger, A. F., and S. Fritz (USWB), 1961: "Cellular Cloud Patterns Revealed by TIROS I," *Tellus,* Vol. 8, No. 1, pp. 1-8.

9-11   Sasaki, Y., 1962: *A Theoretical Explanation of the Convection Mechanism in Cellular Cloud Patterns Revealed by TIROS I Photographic Observations,* Final Report, Contract Cwb 10064, University of Oklahoma.

9-12   Roy, D., and R. S. Scorer, 1962: *Studies of Cellular Convection with Special Reference to the Atmosphere,* Imperial College, London.

9-13   Scorer, R. S., 1963: "The Dynamics of Cloud Formations," *Rocket and Satellite Meteorology,* North-Holland Publishing Company, Amsterdam, pp. 393-405.

9-14   Conover, J. H., 1962: *Cloud Interpretation from Satellite Altitudes,* CR Research Note No. 81, AFCRL. (See G-15).

9-15   Conover, J. H., 1963: Supplement 1 to CR Research Note No. 81, AFCRL.

9-16   Erickson, C. O., and L. F. Hubert, 1961: *Identification of Cloud Forms from TIROS I Pictures,* USWB, Meteorological Satellite Laboratory Report No. 7.

9-17   Cronin, J. F., 1963: *Terrestrial Features of the United States as Viewed from TIROS,* Scientific Report No. 2, Contract No. AF 19(628)-2471, ARACON Geophysics Co.

9-18   Singer, S. F., and R. W. Popham (USWB), 1963: "Non-meteorological Observations from Weather Satellites," *Astronautics and Aerospace Engineering*, Vol. 1, No. 3, pp. 89-92.

9-19   Wark, D. Q., and R. W. Popham, 1962: *Ice Photography from the Meteorological Satellites TIROS I and TIROS II*, USWB Meteorological Satellite Laboratory Report No. 8.

9-20   Wark, D. Q., Popham, R. W., Dotson, W. A., et al., 1962: "Ice Observations by TIROS II Satellite and by Aircraft," *Arctic*, Vol. 15, No. 1, pp. 9-26.

9-21   Wark, D. Q., and R. W. Popham, 1960: "TIROS I Observations of Ice in the Gulf of St. Lawrence," *Monthly Weather Review*, Vol. 88, No. 5, pp. 182-186.

9-22   Merritt, E., 1963: "Can TIROS See Jet Streams?" *Meteorological Satellite System Analyses*, Final Report, Contract No. AF 19(604)-5582, Allied Research Associates, Inc., pp. 3-17.

9-23   Bowley, C. J., A. H. Glaser, R. J. Newcomb, and R. J. Boucher (ARACON Geophysics), 1962: "Satellite Observations of Wake Formation Beneath an Inversion," *J. Atmospheric Sciences*, Vol. 19, No. 1, pp. 52-55.

9-24   Dunn, G. E., 1940: "Cyclogenesis in the Tropical Atlantic," *Bulletin of the American Meteorological Society*, Vol. 21, No. 6, pp. 215-229.

9-25   Riehl, H., 1945: *Waves in the Easterlies and the Polar Front in the Tropics*, University of Chicago, Department of Meteorolgy, Miscellaneous Reports No. 17, Univ. of Chicago Press.

9-26   Sadler, J. C. (USAF), 1963: "Utilization of Meteorological Satellite Cloud Data in Tropical Meteorology," *Rocket and Satellite Meteorology*, North-Holland Publishing Co., Amsterdam, pp. 333-355.

9-27   Hubert, L. F. (USWB), 1961: "A Subtropical Convergence Line of the South Pacific," *J. Geophysical Research*, Vol. 66, No. 3, pp. 797-812.

9-28   Hubert, L. F., 1961: "Tropical Cloudiness, Severe Storms, and Convective Cells," *Proceedings of the International Meteorological Satellite Workshop*, NASA-USWB, U. S. Government Printing Office, pp. 75-89.

9-29   Schuetz, J., and S. Fritz (USWB), 1961: "Cloud Streets over the Carribbean Sea," *Monthly Weather Review*, Vol. 89, No. 10, pp. 375-382.

9-30   Merritt, E., 1963: "TIROS-Revealed African Disturbances Related to Atlantic Hurricanes," *Meteorological Satellite System Analyses*, Final Report, Contract No. AF 19(604)-5582, Allied Research Associates, Inc., pp. 18-47.

9-31   Fritz, S. (USWB), 1962: "Satellite Pictures and the Origin of Hurricane Anna," *Monthly Weather Review*, Vol. 90, No. 12, pp. 507-513.

9-32   Merritt, E., 1964: "Tropical Cyclone Development; A Satellite Derived Interpretation Model," (ARACON Geophysics Company, see 9-G-6).

9-33   Baliles, M. D., and H. Neiss (Editors), 1963: *Conference on Satellite Ice Studies*, Meteorological Satellite Laboratory Report No. 20, USWB, NWSC.

9-34   Ludwig, F. L., and R. E. Nagle, 1960: *Cloud Shield and Radar Precipitation Echo Relationships with Satellite Applications*, Scientific Report No. 1, Contract No. AF 19(604)-5982, Stanford Research Institute.

9-35   Nagle, R. E., R. H. Blackmer, and M. G. H. Ligda, 1960: *Research Directed Toward the Use of Synoptic Radar Observations in the Interpretation of Satellite Cloud Observations*, Technical Progress Report No. 2, Contract No. AF 19(604)-5982, Stanford Research Institute.

9-36   Nagle, R. E., and R. H. Blackmer, Jr., 1961: *Comparisons of Radar Precipitation and Satellite Cloud Observations*, Scientific Report No. 2, Contract AF 19(604)-5982, SRI.

9-37   Nagle, R. E., 1962: *Comparison of Time Integrated Radar Detected Precipitation with Satellite Observed Cloud Patterns*, Scientific Report No. 1, Contract No. AF 19(628)-284, Stanford Research Institute.

9-38   Dennis, A. S., 1963: *Rainfall Determinations by Meteorological Satellite Radar*, Final Report, Contract No. NASr-49(06), Stanford Research Institute.

9-39   Fritz, S., and J. S. Winston (USWB), 1962: "Synoptic Use of Radiation Measurements from Satellite TIROS II," *Monthly Weather Review*, Vol. 90, No. 1, pp. 1-9.

9-40   Nordberg, W., W. R. Bandeen, B. J. Conrath, V. Kunde, and I. Persano (NASA), 1962: "Preliminary Results of Radiation Measurements from TIROS III Meteorological Satellite," *J. Atmospheric Sciences*, Vol. 19, No. 1, pp. 20-30.

9-41   Bandeen, W. R., B. J. Conrath, W. Nordberg, and H. P. Thompson (NASA), 1963: "A Radiation View of Hurricane Anna from the TIROS III Meteorological Satellite," *Rocket and Satellite Meteorology*, pp. 222-233, North-Holland Publishing Company, Amsterdam.

9-42   Rao, P. K., and J. S. Winston (USWB), 1963: "An Investigation of Some Synoptic Capabilities of Atmospheric 'Window' Measurements from Satellite TIROS II," *J. Applied Meteorology*, Vol. 2, No. 1, pp. 12-23.

9-43   Fujita, T., T. Ushijima, W. A. Hass, and G. T. Dellert, Jr., 1963: "Meteorological Interpretation of Convective Nephsystems Appearing in TIROS Cloud Photographs," *Rocket and Satellite Meteorology*, pp. 357-387, North-Holland Publishing Company, Amsterdam.

9-44 Wexler, R., 1962: *Interpretation of TIROS II Radiation Measurements*, Final Report, Contract No. AF 19(604)-5968, Allied Research Associates, Inc.

9-45 Wark, D. Q., G. Yamamoto, and J. H. Lienisch (USWB), 1962: "Methods of Estimating Infrared Flux and Surface Temperature from Meteorological Satellites," *J. Atmospheric Sciences*, Vol. 19, No. 5, pp. 369-384.

9-46 Soberman, R. K., 1963: "Noctilucent Clouds," *Scientific American*, Vol. 208, No. 6, pp. 50-59.

9-47 Wexler, R., 1963: *Synoptic Interpretations and Heat Balance Determinations from TIROS II Radiation Data*, Scientific Report No. 1, Contract No. AF 19(628)-429, ARACON Laboratories.

9-48 Winston, J. S., and P. K. Rao (USWB), 1962: "Preliminary Study of Planetary-Scale Outgoing Long-Wave Radiation as Derived from TIROS II Measurements," *Monthly Weather Review*, Vol. 90, No. 8, pp. 307-310.

9-49 Wark, D. Q., and J. S. Winston (USWB), 1963: "Application of Satellite Radiation Measurements to Synoptic Analysis and to Studies of the Planetary Heat Budget," *Rocket and Satellite Meteorology*, pp. 247-253, North-Holland Publishing Company, Amsterdam.

9-50 Prabhakara, C., and S. I. Rasool, 1963: "Evaluation of TIROS Infrared Data," *Rocket and Satellite Meteorology*, pp. 234-246, North-Holland Publishing Co., Amsterdam.

9-51 Weinstein, M., and V. E. Suomi (U. of Wisconsin), 1961: "Analysis of Satellite Infrared Radiation Measurements on a Synoptic Scale," *Monthly Weather Review*, Vol. 89, No. 11.

9-52 Boucher, R. J., C. J. Bowley, E. S. Merritt, C. W. C. Rogers, P. E. Sherr, and W. K. Widger, Jr., 1963: *Synoptic Interpretations of Cloud Vortex Patterns as Observed by Meteorological Satellites*, Final Report, Contract No. Cwb-10630, ARACON Geophysics Company.

9-53 Merritt, E. S., 1964: "Easterly Waves and Perturbations, A Reappraisal," *Journal of Applied Meteorology*, Vol. 3, No. 4, pp. 367-382.

9-54 Sadler, J. C. (USAF), 1964: "Tropical Cyclones of the Eastern North Pacific as Revealed by TIROS Observations," *Journal of Applied Meteorology*, Vol. 3, No. 4, pp. 347-366.

9-55 Miller, F. R. (USAF), 1963: "An Application of TIROS Cloud Observations in Sparse Data Regions," *Monthly Weather Review*, Vol. 91, No. 9, pp. 433-451.

9-56 Widger, W. K., Jr., 1964: "A Synthesis of Interpretations of Extratropical Vortex Patterns as Seen by TIROS," *Monthly Weather Review*, Vol. 92, No. 6, pp. 263-282.

CHAPTER 10

General

10-G-1 Stampfl, R. A., 1963: *The Nimbus Spacecraft and Its Communication System*, NASA Technical Note D-1422.

10-G-2 Stampfl, R., and H. Press (NASA), 1962: "Nimbus Spacecraft System," *Aerospace Engineering*, Vol. 21, No. 7, pp. 16-28.

10-G-3 Press, H., and J. V. Michaels (NASA), 1963: "Nimbus Spacecraft Development," *Astronautics and Aerospace Engineering*, Vol. 1, No. 3, pp. 42-45.

10-G-4 Goddard Space Flight Center, 1962: *Nimbus*, NASA, U. S. Government Printing Office.

10-G-5 Goddard Space Flight Center, 1962: *Proceedings of the Nimbus Program Review*, November 14-16, 1962, NASA GSFC, Document No. X-650-62-226.

10-G-6 Tepper, M. (NASA), 1961: "NASA Meteorological Satellite Plans for the Future," *Proceedings of the International Meteorological Satellite Workshop*, NASA, USWB, U. S. Government Printing Office, pp. 163-167.

Specific

10-1 Stroud, W. G., 1962: "Introduction to Nimbus," *Proceedings of the Nimbus Program Review*, NASA, GSFC.

10-2 Widger, W. K., Jr., 1960: "A Generalized, Schematic Flow-Chart for the Reduction and Processing of Satellite Meteorological Data," *Contributions to Satellite Meteorology*, GRD Research Notes No. 36, ARCRC.

10-3 Stampfl, R., 1962: "Nimbus Spacecraft System Concept," *Proceedings of the Nimbus Program Review*, NASA, GSFC.

10-4 Goldshlak, L., 1963: *APT Users' Guide*, Scientific Report No. 1, Contract No. AF 19(628)-2471, Allied Research Assoc.

10-5 Butler, H. I. (NASA), 1963: "Nimbus Testing," *Astronautics and Aerospace Engineering*, Vol. 1, No. 3, pp. 46-47.

10-6 Bandeen, W. R., 1961: *Earth Oblateness and Relative Sun Motion Considerations in the Determination of an Ideal Orbit for the Nimbus Meteorological Satellite*, NASA Technical Note D-1045.

CHAPTER 11

General

11-G-1 Panel on Operational Meteorological Satellites, 1961: *Plan for a National Operational Meteorological Satellite System*, (Also reprinted in References 11-G-2, G-3).

11-G-2 Committee on Science and Astronautics, U. S. House of Representatives, 1961: *National Meteorological Satellite Pro-*

gram, Hearings before the Committee, July 25, 26, and 27, 1961, U. S. Government Printing Office.

11-G-3   Subcommittee on Applications and Tracking and Data Acquisition, Committee on Science and Astronautics, U. S. House of Representatives, 1962; *Meteorological Satellites,* Hearings before the Subcommittee, August-September, 1962, U. S. Government Printing Office.

11-G-4   Johnson, D. S., 1961: "An Operational Meteorological Satellite System," *Proceedings of the International Meteorological Satellite Workshop,* NASA-USWB, U. S. Government Printing Office, pp. 169-171.

11-G-5   Johnson, D. S., W. F. Hall, and C. L. Bristor (USWB), 1963: "Nimbus Data in Operational Meteorology," *Astronautics and Aerospace Engineering,* Vol. 1, No. 3, pp. 52-56.

11-G-6   Bristor, C. L. (USWB), 1962: "Processing Satellite Weather Data—A Status Report—Part I," *1962 Fall Joint Computer Conference, AFIPS Conference Proceedings,* Vol. 22, pp. 11-18, Spartan Books, Washington, D. C.

11-G-7   Miller, L. I. (USWB), 1962: "Processing Satellite Weather Data—A Status Report—Part II," *1962 Fall Joint Computer Conference, AFIPS Conference Proceedings,* Vol. 22, pp. 19-26, Spartan Books, Washington, D. C.

11-G-8   Kennedy, John F. (President of the United States), 1961: *Urgent National Needs,* Message to the Congress, May 25, 1961 (H. Doc. No. 174, 87th Congress, 1st Session).

Specific

11-1   Glaser, A. H., and F. E. Christensen, 1963: "TOSS: TIROS Operation Satellite System," *Astronautics and Aerospace Engineering,* Vol. 1, No. 3, pp. 38-41.

11-2   Widger, W. K., Jr., 1960: "A Generalized Schematic Flow-Chart for the Reduction and Processing of Satellite Meteorological Data," *Contributions to Satellite Meteorology,* GRD Research Notes No. 36, AFCRC, pp. 191-203 .

11-3   Cowan, L. W., S. H. Hubbard, and S. F. Singer, 1963: "Direct Readout Weather Satellites," *Astronautics and Aerospace Engineering,* Vol. 1, No. 3, pp. 61-66.

11-4   Widger, W. K., Jr., 1964: "Possible Approach to Cross-Track Radiometric Scanning from a Cartwheel Satellite," *Journal of Spacecraft and Rockets,* Vol. 1, No. 4, pp. 427-429.

CHAPTER 12

General

12-G-1   King-Hele, Desmond, 1960: *Satellites and Scientific Research,* Routledge and Kegan Paul, London (or Dover, N.Y.).

12-G-2   NASA, 1962: "Space Probes and Satellites—General Principles," *Space, The New Frontier,* U. S. Government Printing Office.

Specific

12-1   Bandeen, W. R., 1961: *Earth Oblateness and Relative Sun Motion Considerations in the Determination of an Ideal Orbit for the Nimbus Meteorological Satellite,* NASA Technical Note D-1045.

12-2   Widger, W. K., Jr., and C. P. Wood, 1961: "An Explanation of the Limitations to the Coverage Provided by TIROS," *Weatherwise,* Volume 14, Number 6, pp. 230-237.

12-3   Pyle, R. L., and S. F. Singer, 1963: *An Analysis of CDA Station Effectiveness in Relation to Satellite Orbit,* Meteorological Satellite Laboratory Report No. 18, U. S. Weather Bureau, National Weather Satellite Center.

12-4   Cowan, L. W., S. H. Hubbard, and S. F. Singer, 1963: "Direct Readout Weather Satellites," *Astronautics and Aerospace Engineering,* Vol. 1, No. 3, pp. 61-66.

12-5   Sweeney, W. J., Jr., C. H. Helliwell, Jr., and P. T. Van Aken (Editors), 1963: *MITROS, The MIT Tropical Observation Satellite,* A Preliminary Design and Feasibility Study of an Equatorial Weather Satellite System, MIT Publications Office, Cambridge, Mass.

12-6   Tepper, M. (NASA), 1963: "A Solution in Search of a Problem," *Bulletin of the American Meteorological Society,* Vol. 44, No. 9, pp. 543-548.

12-7   Wood, C. P., 1962: *Highly Elliptical TIROS Orbit,* unpublished NASA GSFC memorandum, August 28, 1962.

12-8   Oseroff, H., 1962: *Preliminary Report on Effects of Highly Eccentric TIROS Orbit,* unpublished NASA GSFC memorandum, August, 1962.

12-9   Cooper, G., 1960: "Orbital Sampling Characteristics," *Meteorological Satellite System Analyses,* Second Semi-Annual Technical Summary Report, Contract No. AF 19(604)-5582, Allied Research Associates, Inc. (also reprinted in Reference G-13, pp. 351-367).

12-10   Gray, T. I., Jr., and S. F. Singer, 1963: *An Investigation of Meteorological Satellite Characteristics for Continuous Earth Coverage,* Meteorological Satellite Laboratory Report No. 19, U. S. Weather Bureau, National Weather Satellite Center.

CHAPTER 13

General

13-G-1   Reichelderfer, F. W., 1963: "WMO Moves into Space,"

Astronautics and Aerospace Engineering, Vol. 1, No. 3, pp. 93-96.

13-G-2   NASA-USWB, 1961: *Proceedings of the International Meteorological Satellite Workshop,* Nov. 13-22, 1961, U. S. Government Printing Office, Washington, D. C.

13-G-3   World Meteorological Organization, 1962: *First Report on the Advancement of Atmospheric Sciences and their Application in the Light of Developments in Outer Space,* Secretariat, WMO, Geneva, Switzerland (Reprinted in 13-G-4).

13-G-4   U. S. House of Representatives, 1962: *Meteorological Satellites,* Hearings before the Subcommittee on Applications and Tracking and Data Acquisition, Committee on Science and Astronautics, U. S. Government Printing Office.

13-G-5   United Nations, 1961: *International Cooperation in the Peaceful Uses of Outer Space,* Resolution adopted by the General Assembly, 1721(XVI). (Reprinted in 13-G-3, -4).

13-G-6   Wexler, H., and J. E. Caskey, Jr., 1963: *Proceedings of the International Symposium on Rocket and Satellite Meteorology,* April 1962, North-Holland Publishing Co., Amsterdam.

13-G-7   Jacobs, W. C., 1962: *Meteorological Satellites,* Staff Report for the Committee on Aeronautical and Space Sciences, U. S. Senate, U. S. Government Printing Office.

13-G-8   Petterssen, S., 1963: *An Outline of International Programs in the Atmospheric Sciences,* A Report by the ad hoc Committee on International Programs in Atmospheric Sciences and Hydrology, National Academy of Sciences, National Research Council, Publication 1085, Washington, D. C.

Specific

13-1   Stewart, George R., 1941: *Storm,* Random House, New York.

13-2   Ludlam, F. H., and L. I. Miller, 1959: *Research on the Properties of Cloud Systems,* Final Report, Contract AF 61(514)-1292, Imperial College of Science and Technology, London.

13-3   Wexler, H. (USWB), 1959: *Satellites and Meteorology: A Report to the World Meteorological Organization.*

13-4   Wexler, H. (USWB), 1960: "Satellites and Meteorology," *WMO Bulletin,* Vol. 9, No. 1, pp. 2-7.

13-5   Tepper, M., 1961: "The Current NASA Meteorological Satellite Program," *Proceedings of the International Meteorological Satellite Workshop,* NASA-USWB, pp. 17-24, U. S. Government Printing Office.

13-6   Baliles, M., and H. Neiss (Editors), 1963: *Conference on Satellite Ice Studies,* Meteorological Satellite Laboratory Report No. 20, U. S. Weather Bureau, National Weather Satellite Center.

13-7   Wexler, H. (USWB), 1962: "Global Meteorology and the United Nations," *Weatherwise*, Vol. 15, No. 4, pp. 141-147, 167.

13-8   Oliver, V. (USWB), 1962: "TIROS Fills a Void for World Weather Watch," *Weatherwise*, Vol. 15, No. 4, pp. 160-162.

13-9   Holloman, J. H., 1963: "The Need and Opportunity for International Cooperation in the Atmospheric Sciences," *Bulletin of the American Meteorological Society*, Vol. 44, No. 5, pp. 305-308.

CHAPTER 14

Specific

14-1   Sweeny, W. J., Jr., C. H. Helliwell, Jr., and P. T. Van Aken (Editors), 1963: *MITROS, The M. I. T. Tropical Observation Satellite*, A Student Project in Systems Engineering performed at M. I. T. during the Spring Term, 1963, M. I. T. Publications Office, Cambridge, Mass.

14-2   Morse, J. G., 1963: "Energy for Remote Areas," *Science,* Vol. 139, No. 3560, pp. 1175-1180.

14-3   Schneebaum, M. I., and R. A. Stampfl (NASA), 1963: "Data Storage for Meteorological Satellites," *Astronautics and Aerospace Engineering*, Vol. 1, No. 3, pp. 48-51.

14-4   Dreyfus, M. G., and D. T. Hilleary, 1962: "Satellite Infrared Spectrometer—Design and Development," *Aerospace Engineering*, Vol. 21, No. 2, pp. 42-45 (also reprinted in *Infrared Instrumentation for Meteorological Satellites*, Bulletin 14-003, Barnes Engineering Company, Stamford, Conn., pp. 28-31).

14-5   Wark, D. Q. (USWB), 1961: "On Indirect Temperature Soundings of the Stratosphere from Satellites," *Journal of Geophysical Research*, Vol. 66, No. 1, pp. 77-82.

14-6   Hanel, R. A., and D. Q. Wark, 1963: "Physical Measurements from Meteorological Satellites," *Astronautics and Aerospace Engineering*, Vol. 1, No. 3, pp. 85-88.

14-7   Battan, L. J., 1962: *Radar Observes the Weather*, Anchor S24, Doubleday & Company, New York.

14-8   Widger, W. K., Jr., and C. N. Touart (USAF), 1957: "Utilization of Satellite Observations in Weather Analysis and Forecasting," *Bulletin of the American Meteorological Society*, Vol. 38, No. 9, pp. 521-533.

14-9   Mook, C. P., and D. S. Johnson, 1959: "A Proposed Weather Radar and Beacon System for Use with Meteorological Radar Satellites," *Proceedings Third National Convention on Military Electronics*, Institute of Radio Engineers, pp. 206-209.

14-10   Keigler, J. E., and L. Krawitz (RCA), 1960: "Weather Radar Observations from an Earth Satellite," *Journal of Geophysical Research*, Vol. 65, No. 9, pp. 2793-2808.

14-11   Katzenstein, H., and H. Sullivan, 1960: "A New Principle for Satellite-Borne Meteorological Radar," *Proceedings Eighth Weather Radar Conference*, American Meteorological Society, pp. 505-515.

14-12   Meteorological Satellite Laboratory, 1961: *Requirements and Design Concepts for an Initial Satellite Weather Radar*, MSL Report No. 4, U. S. Weather Bureau.

14-13   Dennis, A. S., 1963: *Rainfall Determinations by Meteorological Satellite Radar*, Final Report, Project No. 4080, Stanford Research Institute.

14-14   Tepper, M. (NASA), 1963: "A Solution in Search of a Problem," *Bulletin of the American Meteorological Society*, Vol. 44, No. 9, pp. 543-548.

14-15   Nagle, R. E., 1962: *Comparison of Time Integrated Radar Detected Precipitation with Satellite Observed Cloud Patterns*, Scientific Report No. 1, Contract No. AF 19(628)-284, Stanford Research Institute.

14-16   Wanta, R. C., 1951: "Sferics," *Compendium of Meteorology*, American Meteorological Society, pp. 1297-1300.

14-17   Soules, S. D. (Editor), 1962: *Conference on Sferics Measurements from Satellites*, Meteorological Satellite Laboratory Report No. 13, National Weather Satellite Center, U. S. Weather Bureau.

14-18   Moody, A. B., and W. K. Widger, Jr., 1963: "Data Collection by Satellites," *Astronautics and Aerospace Engineering*, Vol. 1, No. 3, pp. 57-58.

14-19   Aiken, J. J., and W. K. Widger, Jr., 1960: "On the Possibility of Measuring Cloud Velocities from a Satellite," *Contributions to Satellite Meteorology*, GRD Research Notes No. 36, AFCRC, pp. 47-61.

14-20   Jones, L. M., F. F. Fischbach, and J. W. Peterson, 1962: "Satellite Measurements of Atmospheric Structure by Refraction," *Planetary and Space Science*, Vol. 9, pp. 351-352.

14-21   Levine, A. K., 1963: "Lasers," *American Scientist*, Vol. 51, No. 1, pp. 14-31.

14-22   Goyer, G. G., and R. Watson, 1963: "The Laser and Its Application to Meteorology," *Bulletin of the American Meteorological Society*, Vol. 44, No. 9, pp. 564-570.

14-23   Lally, V., 1960: "Satellite Satellites—A Conjecture on Future Atmospheric Sounding Systems," *Bulletin of the American Meteorological Society*, Vol. 41, No. 8, pp. 429-432.

14-24   Constant Level Balloon System Study Group, 1962: *A Proposed System for Satellite Tracking of Balloons and Emergencies* (Project STROBE), Joint Meteorological Satellite Advisory Committee.

14-25   Mastenbrook, H. J., and H. D. Cubbage, 1962: *Satellite-*

Tracked Horizontal Sounding System, NRL Memorandum No. 1277.

14-26   Glaser, A. H., 1957: *Meteorological Utilization of Images of the Earth's Surface Transmitted from a Satellite Vehicle,* Final Report under Phase II, Contract No. AF 19(604)-1589, Blue Hill Observatory, Harvard Univ.

14-27   Widger, W. K., Jr., 1960: "A Generalized Schematic Flow-Chart for the Reduction and Processing of Satellite Meteorological Data," *Contributions to Satellite Meteorology,* GRD Research Note No. 36, Air Force Cambridge Research Center, pp. 191-203.

14-28   Collis, R. T. H., and R. E. Nagle, 1963: *Survey of Requirements for a Geophysical Data Collection Satellite System,* Final Report, Contract No. NASr-49(12), Stanford Research Institute.

14-29   Greenfield, S. M., R. E. Huschke, Y. Mintz, R. R. Rapp, and J. D. Sartor, 1962: "A Rationale for Weather Control Research," *Transactions of the American Geophysical Union,* Vol. 43, No. 4, pp. 469-489. (Also reprinted in National Science Foundation, 1963: *Weather Modification,* Fourth Annual Report for the Fiscal Year Ended June 30, 1962, pp. 7-39, U. S. Government Printing Office).

14-30   Kellogg, W. W., and C. Sagan (Editors), 1961: *The Atmosphere of Mars and Venus,* A Report by the ad hoc Panel on Planetary Atmospheres of the Space Science Board, Publication 944, National Academy of Sciences, National Research Council.

14-31   Jones, W. W. (NASA), 1963: "Towards the Synchronous Meteorological Satellite," *Astronautics and Aerospace Engineering,* Vol. 1, No. 3, pp. 59-60.

14-32   Klass, P. J., 1963: "Gravity Gradient Feasibility Test Planned," *Aviation Week and Space Technology,* Vol. 79, No. 22, pp. 79-90.

14-33   Chamberlain, J. W., 1963: "Airglow and the Physics of the Upper Atmosphere," *Science,* Vol. 142, No. 3594, pp. 921-924.

14-34   Chamberlain, J. W., 1961: *Physics of the Aurora and Airglow,* Academic Press, New York.

14-35   Katz, Y. H. (Editor), 1963: *The Application of Passive Microwave Technology to Satellite Meteorology: A Symposium,* Memorandum RM-3401-NASA under Contract No. NASr-21(07), the RAND Corporation.

14-36   Sherr, P. E., and C. W. C. Rogers, *The Identification and Interpretation of Cloud Vortices Using TIROS Infrared Observation,* Final Report, Contract No. Cwb-10812, ARACON Geophysics Company.

Acknowledgments

For the privilege of acquiring the information and experience that made it possible to write this book, I am deeply indebted to many colleagues in the meteorological satellite program. They are too numerous to cite individually. Many of their contributions are, however, cited in the discussions or the references within this book.

There are a few whose contributions cannot be overlooked, even at the inevitable risk of neglecting others equally deserving. They include: Mr. C. N. Touart, my Laboratory Chief at the Geophysics Research Directorate of the Air Force Cambridge Research Center, who made it possible for me to specialize in this field of research, and provided no small amount of both personal encouragement and management skills when the meteorological satellite seemed to be little more than a dream.

Lt. Col. Arthur W. Bostick, then my staff counterpart with the Air Research and Development Command, who was equally helpful in the upper echelons concerned with the initial planning.

My colleagues and successors in the Satellite Meteorology Branch of the Air Force Cambridge Research Laboratories, especially Lt. Col. James C. Sadler.

Dr. Morris Tepper, Director of Meteorological Systems at NASA Headquarters, and his colleagues and the members of his staff, who provided me an indispensable opportunity to view the program as a whole. Especial thanks are due to my immediate staff colleagues there, Mr. Hubert Smith and Miss Teresa Smith.

Mr. William Stroud, Mr. Herbert Butler, and their associates in the Aeronomy and Meteorology Division of NASA's Goddard Space Flight Center, to whom I am indebted for much of what I have learned over the past years about the electronic devices that are so vital to meteorological satellites.

Mr. David S. Johnson, Dr. Sigmund Fritz, and their many fine colleagues of the USWB's National Weather Satellite Center, key associates in practical and research use of the satellite data.

Dr. Arnold H. Glaser, President and Technical Director of ARACON Geophysics Company, and my present immediate colleagues there, who have been of vital assistance to the program for so many years.

For assistance in preparing this book, I am indebted to:

Mr. James V. Bernardo, Director of Educational Programs, NASA Headquarters, who served as the Coordinating Editor of this series and arranged for many of the illustrations used in this book.

Mr. Robert W. White, of ARACON Geophysics Company, for his review of the manuscript and helpful technical suggestions.

Mrs. Carol Rudnicki, for the most excellent and expeditious typings of the manuscript.

Index